BETRAYAL

IN THE
PARSONAGE

BETRAYAL
IN THE
PARSONAGE

Helen Hunter

WINEPRESS WP PUBLISHING

ISBN 1-57921-156-9
Library of Congress Catalog Card Number: 97-68052

ABOUT THE AUTHOR

Helen Hunter is a dynamic and entertaining speaker. She is available to speak at banquets, conferences, retreats, seminars, and media presentations worldwide. For more information, call or write to Helen Hunter at:

1-888-738-1130 or 210-696-7248

Helen Hunter
9859 I–10 West, Box 488
San Antonio, TX 78230

e-mail: tmc96@juno.com

ENDORSEMENTS

"Helen tells a story like nobody I've ever heard before. Colorful, delivered with style and wit! She's like a human billboard."

—Christie Moseley

"Her story-telling and observations about life are much more humorous than most one-liners!"

—Roger Morgan

"Exciting! I kept wanting to know how it ended. Marvelous vocal variety and gestures."

—Lori Bres

"Helen has tremendous breadth of experience and fantastic articulation."

—Rev. Bo Kelly

"The fullness of her subject matter is terrific. It makes me interested in finding out more."

—Eva Thayer

ACKNOWLEDGEMENTS

I'd like to thank the following people for helping me bring this book to fruition:

Heidi Aloe

Joe Barth

Marion Barth

Nina Bodayle

Sylvia Duncan

Paul Drexel

Joni Farr

Sheila Hart

Don Hilkemeier

Patti Jackson

Kelli Kierstaed

Tom Keene

Florence Littauer

Marita Littauer

Linda Longo

Amy McMullan

Mary Dan Menear

Forrest Mims

Karen Park

Marlene Salcher

Bonnie Skinner

Jake Staffel

Gerald Staffel

Sheri Lynn Townsley

Christie Unobagha

Roz Van Meter

Lynn Young

For it was not an enemy that reproached me;
Then I could have borne it:
Neither was it he that hated me
That did magnify himself against me;
Then I would have hid myself from him:

But it was thou, . . . mine equal,
My guide, and mine acquaintance.
We took sweet counsel together,
And walked unto the house of God in company.

Psalm 55:12–14 KJV

CHAPTER 1

B read and cheese at my place then?" asked Madeleine, as the double-decker bus lunged toward us on Princes Street.

"That'll be nice," I said. "I'll be over by seven. I have to stop at the library and finish my translation first."

Madeleine stepped onto the bus and spun around to wave at me. The bus pulled away from the curb and labored up the hill toward the dark silhouette of Edinburgh Castle, high up on Castle Rock. I braced myself against the wintry blast and turned my steps toward the library.

It was the early seventies. I was a first-year student at the university; Madeleine was a year ahead of me. She shared a flat with three men. I never did understand how that worked. I didn't quite know how to ask her about it, nor did she ever offer to explain.

Madeleine's flat was on the upper floor of a typical nine-teenth-century row of gray stone houses with tall windows overlooking the street below. As with all the others, it had high ceilings and was cold and drafty.

One of her roommates answered my ring at the door. Madeleine wandered out of her bedroom, where incense was burning, and invited me into the kitchenette. It was filthy. Dirty dishes were piled sky-high, and some shopping bags were on the wooden table.

"It's Jeremy's turn this week," said Madeleine, by way of explanation. Opening the paper bags, she pulled out a bunch of fat green grapes, a loaf of French bread and a large Camembert cheese. We sat down to eat.

Madeleine was an aristocratic hippie with a posh English accent. She camouflaged her rather large build by wearing baggy Laura Ashley clothes and loose-fitting mackintoshes. She draped herself with trendy oriental jewelry and tied silk scarves over her soft brown hair. Her face was oval and pale with a thin-lipped smile and a large forehead. Her phlegmatic personality matched her casual looks.

One of her roommates started plucking his guitar in a room nearby. Madeleine looked up and smiled dreamily at the sound of the music. Her eyes were a light brown with delicate eyelashes.

I was fascinated by Madeleine. She seemed to float along on her own cloud, unencumbered by the constraints of society and the dictates of traditional morality. She had mentioned nonchalantly that she slept with men when she felt like it, and although I didn't approve of her lifestyle, I was intrigued by the fact that she seemed to experience no guilt. Having been raised in a Catholic convent, I was too modest even to accompany her to a women's sauna, much less to imagine myself living and sleeping with men.

The guitar music in the next room came to an abrupt halt, and heavy footsteps made their way down the hall to the front door, which soon slammed shut, thrusting Madeleine back to reality. She cut herself a piece of cheese and looked up at me.

"So, Helen, how do you like the interpreting program?"

"I love it," I said. "It's so exciting sitting in those booths. I can just picture what it's like in the United Nations." I picked a grape and popped it into my mouth.

"I prefer the translating part," said Madeleine, biting carefully into the gooey Camembert cheese. A couple of bread crumbs stuck to her thin lips. "I like to meditate on the meanings of words," she said, licking the crumbs off with her tongue, "and play around with several different possibilities of saying the same thing before I make up my mind."

Our program was designed to train us for a position with an international organization in Geneva, Brussels, or New York. Each month we focused on a specific field, so we would become familiar with the jargon. Science, medicine, space exploration, economics, international politics, law, world organizations, and philosophy were among the subjects in the curriculum.

All the speeches, and all the newspaper articles and trade journals we interpreted and translated, revolved around the theme of the month. We each had to be fluent in two foreign languages; mine were French and Spanish.

Occasionally, our professors would pull out tapes of great orators, such as General de Gaulle or Sir Winston Churchill, for us to interpret. Every day we spent hours practicing in the language lab. We started with short, easy speeches, and progressed to longer, more difficult ones. The professors listened to us constantly and taped every word we spoke.

"Have you decided where you're going next year?" I asked Madeleine. Our third year was to be spent abroad, so we could absorb the culture and write our dissertations.

"I'm definitely going to Mexico City. Latin America is so mysterious and romantic. I've always fantasized about going to see the pyramids."

"I want to go to Mexico City too," I said. "Maybe if we plan it right, we could both be there at the same time."

I went to the sink for a glass of water and then sat back down, carefully folding my black-checkered mini-skirt under me. Although Madeleine and I were of the same height, coloring and complexion, we dressed very differently. I wore platform shoes, black pantyhose called "tights," miniskirts, and bright woolen sweaters. My hair was short and trendy. I wore light makeup; she didn't.

"What do you think you'll do when you graduate?" I asked.

"I'm not sure yet," said Madeleine. "How about you?"

"Oh, I'm going to be a missionary."

"A missionary? Really?"

"Yes. I've wanted to be a missionary in Latin America for years. I might even become a Wycliffe Bible translator. Dr. Eugene Nida came to our class last month to talk about their work. They live among indigenous tribes around the world and translate the Bible."

"But aren't missionaries supposed to be called? How can you know that God is calling you? I mean, how do you know you haven't just made it up?"

"It kind of grows on you. Several things have happened in my life that seem to be pointing me in that direction. When I was twelve, the nuns at my convent school told me about teaching in Africa. I decided then that I really wanted to be a missionary. At age eighteen, I went to French Cameroon and worked in a Presbyterian mission school, teaching English for a year. I absolutely loved it, and knew that being a missionary was what I wanted to do with my life."

"Well, I'm open-minded, but I'm not sure I believe in God and all that religious mumbo jumbo."

"It really boils down to personal experience, Madeleine. Once you've met God, it's as if the light has been turned on in a dark room. A lot of things suddenly become very clear."

I liked talking to Madeleine. I could talk to her about anything, even my doubts and frustrations. She seemed to be more open than most; more understanding. When I talked to other people who didn't believe in God, they didn't seem to have any room for Him. On the other hand, when I tried to explore new ideas with people who did believe in God, I often found them to be too closed-minded. Madeleine was a good listener. In her I found the freedom and acceptance I needed to ponder the mysteries of life.

As the school year came to a close, Madeleine and I decided to leave Edinburgh for a few days. After much talking and planning, we selected to go to Pitlochry, in the Scottish Highlands. We could reach Pitlochry by bus and stay at the youth hostel for next to nothing. We put on our corduroy trousers and packed our rucksacks full of warm clothes and books.

The bus wound its way past the hill called The Mound. Beneath us, a park ran alongside the railway tracks. The lawn was dotted with sun worshipers watching a band playing in the bandstand. Next to the park, tourists were jostling on the pavement, making their way from one elegant shop to another. Beyond Princes Street were the Georgian law offices and banks, and far in the distance glistened the blue North Sea.

"When the sun shines in Edinburgh, it's one of the most beautiful cities I've ever seen!" I said. Madeleine mumbled her assent as she settled back to catch up on her sleep. I didn't want to miss a thing.

The elegant three-story hotels and office buildings soon gave way to the gray-pink stone bungalows of the suburbs. Before long, we were speeding along the country lanes that took us higher and higher, past pastureland and flowing brooks, up to the town of Pitlochry.

The Pitlochry music festival was in progress when we arrived in the little Scottish mountain community. We bought tickets to that evening's concert and went to explore the town. The gray stone streets were swarming with Scotsmen in their kilts, and everywhere, tourists were buying woolen sweaters and lambskin coats. There was a festive atmosphere in the air, and we were thrilled to be able to participate in the cultural events.

After the concert, we crawled into our freshly pressed sheets at the youth hostel. We had a lovely private room, just for the two of us. The furnishings were of polished wood; the blankets of pure wool. Madeleine picked the top bunk, and I slept below.

The following morning, we went for a long walk in the sunshine and sat down on a hill overlooking a green meadow. Below us cattle grazed calmly beside a bubbling brook.

"It was in a meadow just like this that I first experienced God," I told her. Madeleine seemed to like hearing about God. She did not believe in Him, but she was always open to whatever I had to say, and of course, I was eager to share what I knew with her.

"I was fourteen years old, lying back and brooding over my problems," I continued. "Suddenly, the atmosphere became kind of electric, and I was overcome with a Presence

I had never experienced before. I started reading the Bible after that to learn more about God. A couple of years later, I understood that Christ had died for me personally, and I gave Him my life."

"Wow," said Madeleine.

"Yes. It felt great at the time, and I thought my life would be wonderful from then on."

"Well, wasn't it?"

"No, actually it got worse. I wanted to attend a Protestant church where they taught the Bible. My mother was a staunch Catholic, and objected vehemently. My father supported her. They told me I was hallucinating and had been brainwashed by a cult. They said the people in the Protestant church were ignorant, and that if I joined them instead of remaining a Catholic, I would no longer be their child."

"So what did you do?"

"I've agonized about it for several years, but my faith is very important to me, and I plan to join a Protestant church."

"Why would you care so much what church you are in?" she wanted to know.

"Because I realize that I learned to know God by hearing what the Bible has to say about Him. In the Catholic church that I grew up in, they did not read the Bible at all. It was so cluttered with saints and statues and lace and incense that I could not find God there, and that's why I don't want to go back."

"So God is important enough for you to risk being disowned by your parents?"

"Yes, He is. I am their firstborn. They expect great things from me and love it when I perform well in school and do what they want me to do. But whenever I have opinions that differ from theirs, especially about religion and about being a missionary, they just trample on my dreams.

"How do you feel about your parents now?"

"I've stopped sharing my hopes and dreams with them. I feel so sad that this has come between us, but I keep hoping they will understand.

"Do you think they will let you go to Mexico City for your year abroad?"

"Oh, yes. They are proud of my studies, but they are still determined that I will not be a missionary and live in South America. They think I'm going through a phase and that I will outgrow it. But I've felt called to be a missionary since I was twelve years old, and there's nothing else I'd rather do."

We sat in that field in deep discussion as I poured out my heart to Madeleine. I told her how much pain I had experienced in being ostracized by my parents because of my faith, and she seemed to understand. I had kept my heartache a secret from most people, and it felt good to let it out and tell her all about it.

Finally, the afternoon clouds rolled over us, and heavy raindrops forced us to run for shelter. My sharing had brought us even closer together. With her friendship and support, the future didn't seem so overwhelming.

CHAPTER 2

During my second year of interpreting school, Madeleine went overseas, and I took the opportunity to make new friends. Just months before I was due to fly away to Mexico City, I met Calvin.

Calvin was a student of political science. He had a keen interest in the world, and a gentleness of spirit that I was curiously drawn to. His fiery red hair and freckles denoted his Scottish ancestry. He wore lambs' wool sweaters and soft suede shoes and had a gentle touch.

At first, Calvin and I talked a lot about the world and about religion. We discussed our homework together, ate our meals together, and went to church together. Then we started meeting in his dormitory to pray for our friends and their problems. Before long, we were kneeling by his bed, and then kneeling closer and closer together. The intimacy of prayer led to the warmth of holding hands, and even an occasional kiss. Before we knew it, we thought we were in love.

One evening in the early spring, Calvin proposed to me. It happened in rather a strange way.

I was sitting on his bed in his cozy dorm room, and he mumbled something about a diamond ring . . . getting the money out of savings. His face turned red, and he seemed awkward and embarrassed.

"You mean, you're asking me to marry you?" I finally asked to help him out of his misery. I hoped I wasn't jumping to the wrong conclusion. A marriage proposal did seem a little premature.

"Yes," he replied, relieved. His face flushed, and his black eyes burned.

I was quite taken aback by this unexpected turn of events. Still in a state of surprise, I said "Yes." I really had no idea what marriage meant, but several of my friends had diamond rings and were looking forward to a future of wedded bliss. I imagined that this was what getting engaged must be all about. I was emotionally attached to Calvin. He was a very nice young man. We seemed to get along, and I felt very special that he would want to hold hands with me and marry me.

The following weekend, Calvin took me to his hometown to meet his family. They lived in a spotless house in a sparkling little Scottish town. They were a good, clean-living, Presbyterian family, and they were obviously very proud of Calvin. I easily passed their inspection, and with their blessing, we returned to Edinburgh to look at engagement rings.

We wandered from shop to shop, gazing at the beautiful diamonds, sapphires, and rubies shining in the windows, looking for just the perfect one to symbolize our future together. Yet despite much gazing, Calvin never seemed to make a final selection, and I felt it would be presumptuous of me to tell him what I wanted.

In Scotland, people were taught to act very surprised and undeserving when being given a gift. The protocol was to resist politely many times over and finally acquiesce after much protest. This was supposed to show humility and true gratitude. I had lived in several cultures while growing up and had learned to adapt to the mores of the people around me. So even though I had very definite ideas of what I liked in a ring and how I expected the future to look, I felt constrained to keep my peace and wait for Calvin to unfold the future for me.

At the next break, Calvin came with me to London to meet my parents. I knew that this visit would not be easy. My mother and father had grown up in Czechoslovakia during the '20s and '30s. They had very conservative ideas about what they expected of me, including of course, a Catholic wedding.

Calvin was a Scottish Presbyterian, a branch of Christianity at the opposite end of the spectrum from the Catholic faith. For me, as for my parents, it was important that my suitor ask for my hand in marriage. I did not expect their blessing, but I did want to know I was choosing a brave man who would rescue me from their influence and whisk me off to live happily ever after in his kingdom, as did the princes in the fairy tales.

Surprisingly, Calvin's visit came and went, but he left London without having said a word about our engagement to my parents.

I was puzzled.

Calvin knew that I had to spend a year abroad, and he said he would wait for me. He promised to keep in touch, and I gave him a long list of addresses where he could reach me as I travelled around the United States on a Greyhound bus for two months. I was afraid I would miss him terribly.

Going to America was thrilling. I flew all night long and landed at Kennedy Airport in New York at about four o'clock in the morning. As I dragged my suitcase through the airport, I was delighted to see a sign that read Ladies' Restroom. *How considerate of the American people*, I thought, *to provide a place for weary transatlantic travelers to lie down and sleep.* I pushed the door open, and much to my dismay, found no beds to lie down on—just a row of toilet stalls and sinks.

Some of my mother's friends came to pick me up, and as we drove out of the airport and down the main boulevard, I was horrified to see a building with a big sign on it that said BODY SHOP. I didn't know whether it was a house of prostitution or a cadaver shop for medical students! My hosts laughed and told me that it was a car repair shop. Evidently, there was a lot about the American language that I didn't know!

America was quite different from what I had imagined. I expected every city to consist of huge skyscrapers and to be filled with gangsters. Instead, I found a massive land of one-story suburban homes and lots and lots of billboards. The people all seemed so honest and good; they didn't even lock their doors at night. I felt very welcome and very safe.

My only disappointment, as I stayed with family friends from New York, up the east coast to Canada, across the Midwest, and then down to Florida, was that I did not receive a single letter from Calvin. I wrote to him from every stop. There simply was no answer. Every time I arrived at a new address, I hoped news was there, but it wasn't, and I was worried.

Finally, when I arrived in Florida, there was a letter in Calvin's handwriting waiting for me. I could hardly wait to run to my room and read it. The letter went something like this:

Dear Helen:

    I have felt very uncomfortable about our engagement since you left. I am a conservative person. I just want to settle down and have a family. You, on the other hand, are an adventuress. You want to see the world. You are too exotic for me. After much soul-searching, I have decided to break off our engagement. I wish you all the best.

                    Calvin

PS: I never did like the clothes you wore, anyway.

I was furious. I was hurt. All these months of dreaming about marrying him, and suddenly it was over! I couldn't believe that he would be such a coward as to end an engagement with a letter! And the gall to tell me that he hadn't liked my clothes!

I had been letting my hair grow really long for the wedding. I went straight to the beauty shop and had it cut short. I had been planning to take a bus the long way to Mexico City. I bought a plane ticket instead, anxious to put Calvin behind me and get on with my life.

As the plane took off, I leaned my seat back and let my mind wander. I was tired of British men who couldn't make decisions. Not just Calvin, but all the young men I had gone out with.

"Where do you want to go? What do you want to do?" they would ask, politely. I wanted someone decisive who knew what he wanted and who invited me along, instead of simply catering to my whims.

I was tired of serious intellectuals who philosophized the night away. I wanted romance. I wanted someone to buy me roses. Someone to take me to a movie. Someone to love me for who I was. Someone to have a good time with. I wanted to laugh, to do things people are supposed to do when they are in love: kiss, hold hands, dream, and enjoy life!

CHAPTER 3

The clouds began to dissipate as I looked out of the window at the gleaming Caribbean Sea. Every now and then I could see a cruise ship glistening in the sun. After a while, land came into view, and we flew over a series of mountain ranges that went higher, and higher, and higher. Finally, a wide plateau, filled with matchbox-size houses in assorted bright colors, opened up. We began to swoop down. I was caught up in the mystery of Mexico City, which I had for so long wished to see, and I was ready for a new adventure.

As I checked through Mexican immigration, the official at the desk asked for my papers. My visa had been filled out by hand by a representative of the Mexican Consulate in London. The immigration official insisted on typing the written answers into the visa, directly above the handwritten responses. He pecked out the letters on a rusty old typewriter.

All the other passengers were long gone. I had no choice but to wait patiently.

"Here we are, Señorita," he said at last. "Take this to our office downtown, and they will issue you a six-month student visa."

"Thank you," I said, pulling my luggage out to the curbside telephone to call Madeleine. Our plan to overlap had worked. I had managed to fly out in time to see her for a few weeks before she had to go back to Scotland, and she had agreed to show me the ropes.

"Madeleine! I just landed!" I said excitedly, when she came to the phone.

"Get a taxi and tell him to take you to Polanco. I'll leave the window open. Tell him to honk when you get here. I'll come down and let you in."

The sun was shining brightly as the cab driver fought his way through the afternoon traffic. Everything about Mexico City's bustle was stimulating. Everything was new and in vivid colors. It was teeming with humanity, packed cars and buses, tall skyscrapers, smog. This was my first experience of the Latin American culture, and it held an air of excitement and mystery for me.

Madeleine hugged me warmly. She gave me a yogurt, and we animatedly exchanged the latest news. She promised she would take some time off, so we could go together to the Pyramids of the Sun and the Moon and the Volcano of Popocatépetl, just outside the city.

We went down to the street to buy a newspaper and some mangos at the pavement fruit stand. A couple of folk dancers in brightly colored Aztec costumes danced by, playing a flute and beating a replica of an ancient drum. A garbage truck stopped to pick up the day's pickings. A beggar woman held out her hand for a coin.

"So what are your plans, Helen?" Madeleine asked, as we settled down in her kitchen for a nice, long talk.

"My first project is to visit the Wycliffe Bible Translators' headquarters and see if I like their work. They learn the languages of tribes that do not as yet have a written Bible. Once they learn the language, they create an alphabet and reduce the language to writing. Then they teach the people to read and translate the Bible for themselves. I thought maybe I would enjoy doing that myself."

"Whatever happened with your church membership? Did you ever become a Protestant?" she asked.

"Yes, as a matter of fact, I did, and my parents were furious. They said I betrayed them, and I don't belong in the family anymore."

"How do you feel about that?"

"Really hurt. Rejected. Disappointed," I said, conscious of my own heartache. "I see them as little as possible, because they keep telling me how wrong I am and that I'd be throwing away all my talents to become a missionary."

"So what will you do?"

"Keep praying that they'll stop being angry with me and keep pursuing my dream of being a missionary."

"Well, I hope it all works out for you," said Madeleine, as understanding as always.

I took the shiny, modern subway to the south of town and walked along the cobbled streets past colorful street vendors to the Wycliffe campus. Mr. Klassen, the white-haired campus director, was expecting me. He whirled his executive chair around and stood to greet me, his warm, blue eyes smiling.

"Hello, Helen. I've been expecting you. Come in, and let me take you on a tour," he invited. He was so welcoming that I fell in love with him and his wife immediately and gladly accepted their invitation to visit them often.

My second project was to find a church. At Wycliffe's recommendation, I went directly to a large downtown congregation, where I heard that a famous Argentinean evangelist, Dr. Fernando Vangioni, was holding a week of special revival meetings.

I was mesmerized. Dr. Vangioni carried us to the heights of joy and to the depths of despair in his exposition of the Bible. Madeleine just had to come. I would insist on it.

I met Madeleine for lunch the following day. She was making eyes at a hippielike Scandinavian eating at a table nearby. She said she was looking for a man to travel with her to the Yucatan Peninsula to see the Mayan ruins before she left the country, and the long-haired young man looked like a good candidate.

"But you don't even know the guy!" I said, horrified.

"Well, we can get to know each other on the trip!" she answered, unperturbed. "He obviously doesn't speak Spanish, and I do. I can do all the talking, and he can protect me."

"Protect you! My foot! He'll just as soon rape you!"

"Oh, Helen! Stop being so negative! Give the guy a chance, will you?"

Madeleine was wearing one of her oriental scarves on her head and a gypsy skirt. Frankly, they looked like a good match.

"Listen, Madeleine," I continued, trying to change the subject. "There is a fantastic evangelist speaking at my church tonight. Please come with me, just this once, before you go on your trip."

"Well, if you insist. Just this once. Tell me where it is, and I'll meet you there."

I caught a taxi to the church early that night. I wanted to get a good seat and hold a place for Madeleine. As usual, she was running late. The choir opened with some enthusiastic hymns, the soloist sang a heart-rending song, and the ushers passed the collection plate. Madeleine was still nowhere to be seen. I hoped against hope that she would make it before the sermon began.

Finally, just as Dr. Vangioni got up to speak, Madeleine slipped down the aisle and into the pew beside me. *Thank God*, I thought. Now, I hoped she would listen. Even though she seemed happy with her life, I knew that she had some frustrations, and of course, I wanted her, too, to have a personal relationship with God.

Dr. Vangioni chose that particular evening to describe the horrors of hell. He spared no detail, and before his sermon was over, we could all picture ourselves standing before God at the last judgment.

"What will you say to Him when you face Him?" Vangioni was thundering. "Are you prepared to face eternal torment away from His presence, or will you take Jesus Christ as your personal Savior and accept his death for your sins? Come as you are, come to the rails, and kneel before Him. Tonight, you can be saved. It doesn't matter what kind of life you have lived. Come to the altar tonight and accept His forgiveness."

The organ began to play softly, and Dr. Vangioni invited us to close our eyes and pray. When I looked up again, the aisles were flooded with people. To my great relief and amazement, Madeleine had risen imperceptibly from her seat beside me and was kneeling at the altar, her head bowed. Vangioni issued some final instructions, and slowly, the people began to leave the sanctuary.

I sat in my pew in awe. Madeleine knelt at the rail for a long time. The people trickled quietly out of the building, and the organist packed up his music and left.

After what seemed like an eternity, Madeleine stood up and walked slowly back to my pew. She wiped a tear from her eye with her long silk scarf, and I hugged her. We were both too overcome with emotion to talk. Too relieved to break the silence, we sat down and stared at the altar.

"May we help you, Señoritas?"

Before us stood two young men. Both were tall, well-dressed, and brown-skinned. The taller one had a slight curl in his hair, denoting Spanish ancestry, while his companion had the slick dark hair of the Mexican Indian. They looked at us intently.

Madeleine was still in a daze from the evening's events.

"I just accepted Christ," she mumbled.

"It's getting late," interjected the taller one with the curly hair. "May we escort you to your bus stop?"

He had an athletic build with wide shoulders and a sparkling white smile. He wore a blue-striped, polyester suit, a tie, and a neatly pressed, lemon yellow shirt. His almond-shaped brown eyes were intense and penetrating. His lips were full, his nose a little flat; his blue-black hair was thick and curly. He looked unlike anyone I had ever known. His manner was attentive, and there was a sense of pride in his erect posture.

Outraged by the intrusion into our privacy, I stood to face him. His eyes were deep pools of brown, his expression disarming and disquieting. I wasn't sure I wanted to trust him.

"Please, Señoritas," said the other young man. He wore a shiny brown suit and a green tie. "It's not good for you to walk the streets alone at this time of the evening."

"Allow us to introduce ourselves," continued the first one. "My name is José Mendez, and this is my cousin, Alberto. We are members of the church here and leaders of the youth. It would be a pleasure for us to escort you home."

I was too startled to protest. We made our way down the stairs to the church lobby.

"So where are you two pretty ladies from—the United States?" asked José.

"No, we're from the United Kingdom," volunteered Madeleine, always quick to socialize with strangers. I was being much more circumspect. Madeleine had just accepted Christ, and the last thing I thought we needed right then was a date!

The traffic was heavy, and the evening crowds were jostling to catch the packed buses in the dark. We made our way down the narrow side street toward Reforma Avenue. The crowds broke up our party. José moved quickly to my side, and Alberto to Madeleine's.

José was talking incessantly, slowly bringing me out of my introspective mood. I decided to let him talk. I wasn't sure what to think of him.

My first impression was that he was a ladies' man. There was something about the look in his eye and his flowery words that made me wonder how many other women he had flattered. Or was that just the Latin way? Being in a different culture, I wasn't sure whether to trust my instincts, or give him the benefit of my ignorance.

But José worked hard at disarming my initial distrust. He asked me about my studies. He seemed familiar with many of the books I had read, both in Spanish and English, and he had seen many of the movies popular in Britain that year. I was surprised at his level of education and the intelligence he exhibited in conversation; it didn't seem to match his modest appearance.

"What are you studying?" he asked me.

"I'm studying interpreting and translating. I'm going to write a dissertation in Spanish about religious syncretism in Mexico. I'm planning to spend some time in the Museum of Anthropology, and then I want to visit some of the indigenous tribes to interview them about their customs."

"Oh, how interesting," said José. "I work in a small town about two hours from here, and my grandparents still live in the village nearby. I'll take you to meet them one of these days." He said he was studying for his master's in education at night. He taught school in an outlying village by day and preached in remote Indian churches on Sundays.

Before we knew it, we had passed the bus stop and were strolling down the wide Reforma Avenue. Madeleine and Alberto were deep in conversation, and José took my elbow as we crossed the busy side streets and passed the Russian Embassy.

"I used to love to come here as a child and watch films from the Soviet-bloc countries. I had a crush on a beautiful Russian actress when I was about nine years old, and I always dreamed of marrying a Slav."

I didn't tell him that my mother and father were both originally from Czechoslovakia, which made my blood one-hundred percent Slav. I didn't want to give him any ideas.

At the end of Reforma Avenue, the young men put us in a taxi and instructed it to take us back to Madeleine's in Polanco. We went upstairs, and I made myself a cup of tea. I sat down in the kitchen to review the evening's events.

On the one hand, I felt as if the arrival of the two young men was an intrusion into my cozy relationship with Madeleine, and I wondered why I was so resistant to getting to know them. On the other hand, I was still stunned that Madeleine had actually gone forward and accepted Christ! I hoped she would cancel her plans for the Yucatan and stay for the rest of the revival.

Much to my relief, she did. Not only did we go to the pyramids together, but we attended every service. I decided I should be a little more open minded, so we spent each evening after the service, walking down the avenue with José and Alberto.

By the time the campaign was over, we four had become fast friends. Alberto was heartbroken when Madeleine had to leave Mexico City and return to Edinburgh.

CHAPTER 4

With Madeleine gone, it was time for me to find my own room to rent. I picked up a local paper, and set off by subway to check out the available options. I wasn't prepared for the mobs in the underground. It was hot and sticky, and the men made a point of standing uncomfortably close to me.

The first place I visited looked like a convent. Iron gates guarded the young ladies from intruders. There was a ten o'clock curfew, and all meals had to be eaten in a dining room, supervised by a prim, old spinster. I moved on.

The second place was in a central part of town. I was admitted up a steep flight of stairs and into an apartment with the rooms painted black. In each room there was a big bed, and on it lay curlers and silk scarves. It wasn't long before I realized I was in a house of prostitution, so I turned that room down too.

In desperation, I asked my classmates at the university for help. One of them said he knew of a widow in an elegant part of the city who was renting out her maid's quarters. She lived on the sixth floor of a skyscraper off the main avenue. As soon as I met her, I felt safe and wanted there, so I took the "room with bath attached."

Soon after the beginning of the semester, the church organized a weekend retreat for the youth. José picked me up after school on Friday and took me by taxi to the church, where we piled into a rickety old bus. He introduced me to several young women who covered their mouths and giggled in embarrassment. Two of them were his sisters. We sat near them as the bus chugged slowly along in the heavy rush-hour traffic. The young women kept looking at me and smiling shyly whenever I looked in their direction.

The classy stores and high-rise apartment buildings gradually gave way to suburbs of concrete homes painted in outrageously wild colors, messy-looking store fronts, and finally, to unfinished shanties. People lived in dwellings of gray blocks, iron posts, and corrugated tin roofs, hastily thrown together and never finished. The streets were no longer paved, and puddles stood everywhere. Children played in them undaunted, and every once in a while, a woman with a multi-colored plastic shopping bag could be seen clutching her sweater and maneuvering her way home through the mud.

The sun, a glowing ball, was setting in the misty sky above the inactive volcanoes that formed the plateau. Mud huts, surrounded by fields of cacti, began to appear. Here and there, a lonely Indian in colorful garb was scurrying home, his bare feet clad only in cheap, plastic sandals.

The bus rattled along a gravel road through the tall fields of corn and past some crude stone fences. The ruins of a large stone farmhouse, probably a remnant of colonial days, came into view, and the bus heaved to a standstill.

José's sisters and their friends were all talking at once. The excitement was contagious. Everyone pushed and shoved, wanting to get off at once.

Inside, the farmhouse was bare. There was a huge, rustic kitchen with a primitive oven and big cauldrons. Next to it was a dining room with some simple wooden tables and benches, and off to the side was a stack of old mattresses.

"Girls, upstairs! Boys, stay down here!" yelled one of the chaperones. I followed the girls up a steep staircase of uneven stone steps to an empty room with a stack of mattresses in the corner.

The girls were most anxious to stake their claim to a mattress. Apparently, there were some good mattresses and some others that were very worn out.

"Here, Helena! Take this one! You can sleep next to me!" said Olga, a cheerful soul who had taken it upon herself to make me feel at home and act as my guide and protector.

The other girls had already grabbed their mattresses and were pulling them into position. It wasn't long before the entire floor space was covered with mattresses and girls' paraphernalia. Olga patted her mattress approvingly and then plunked herself down. She was wearing a thick, woven shawl over her brown polyester pants.

"I wonder what time they'll make us go to bed," she mumbled to herself, rolling her eyes. "I have to curl my hair and finish reading my comic strip before lights out."

I positioned my mattress next to hers, put my blanket and bags down on it, and went downstairs to a simple meal preceded by prayer and followed by the singing of choruses. José invited me to step outside for a few minutes to look at the stars, and then it was time for bed.

"Wake up! Wake up!"

Olga was shaking me. Several of the other girls were leaning over my mattress urging me to get up.

"Quick, Helena! Go look out the window!"

"I'm sleepy. I'll go later," I mumbled. "Is it time to get up?"

"Go to the window. Look outside! You have to!"

I could hear a band of singers and guitars outside. I wondered what was going on. The girls dragged me to the window in my nightie. I pushed on the stiff pane and looked out.

To my horror, there were about twenty young men in the courtyard below. They were all looking up at our window, strumming their guitars and singing. José was in the front row. He was singing, holding one hand up toward me, the other on his heart. I was mortified and pulled away immediately.

"You can't leave the window, Helena. It's a Mexican custom. José and the young men are serenading you. If you walk away, you'll insult them."

I went back to the window and looked out again. José was singing his heart out. I felt so humiliated; I just wanted to die.

When the ordeal was over, the girls all crowded around me.

"You're so lucky! I wish I were the one to be serenaded!" said Bernardina.

"Yes," added Aurea. "When I heard them starting to sing, I hoped against hope that it was for me. My little sister was serenaded last summer, and I've been hoping that my turn will come soon. I'm still waiting."

"It's not fair!" Alicia piped in. "I'd do anything to be serenaded."

"I was serenaded by Jorge," said Maria proudly. "He and a couple of his friends actually hired a band of mariachis. They showed up at my house and woke up the whole neighborhood. My parents were so proud of me. They told me to put on my pretty red cape and step out on the balcony."

"I've always dreamed of being serenaded," said Olga. "I guess I'll keep dreaming. You don't know how lucky you are, Helena!"

I excused myself from the bubbly group of girls and made my way to the rustic shower. When I emerged, several of the girls were blow-drying their hair.

"Can anyone lend me a blow-dryer?" yelled Olga.

"Sure, help yourself," I answered. "There's one in my blue shoulder bag."

Olga came over to my mattress and started to rummage around in my bag while I was putting my socks on.

"Helena!" Olga hissed at me in a whisper. "What are these tampons doing in your bag?"

"I brought them with me just in case," I answered, wondering what the secret was.

"You use tampons? That's awful! Don't let anyone know. Mexican girls don't use tampons. Only loose women do!"

"Oh?" I said, mystified.

"Yes," she explained. "How else can you prove you are a virgin, and why would anyone marry you if you are not?" She looked at me defiantly, as if the answer to her question was obvious.

"I never thought about it that way, Olga. I've been using tampons since I was fourteen years old. Everyone uses them where I come from."

"Well, not here!" said Olga firmly. "So take my advice and hide them, before anyone else finds out."

I put on my white top and blue miniskirt and combed my newly cut, shoulder-length brown hair. Pulling out my mirror, I dabbed a little gray shadow around my greenish-gray eyes and selected a natural pink lipstick to contrast with my healthy tan. Still thinking about my conversation with Olga, I pulled on my knee-highs, grabbed my Bible, and headed toward the stairs.

When I reached the top of the stairs, I stopped short. José was standing at the bottom of the stairs, looking up at me. I started down the uneven steps, feeling a little self-conscious.

"I've dreamed about you all my life," he said.

"Oh, come on!" I responded.

"No. I'm serious. I have. I've had this dream over and over. I'm running through the woods, chasing a girl with shoulder-length brown hair. She's wearing a blue skirt, a white top, and knee-high socks. I've never been able to see her face in my dreams, but when you appeared at the top of the stairs just now, I suddenly knew it was you."

I didn't know what to say. It's true that I had said I was ready for love, but I didn't expect it to show up in the form of this perplexing young man. On the one hand, José appeared to be so incredibly different from me, and I was embarrassed by his expressions of romance. On the other hand, he seemed to be so genuine and expressive. He shared his secret feelings and his dreams openly and hid nothing from me.

Yet was I really ready for love? His world was so startlingly different from mine that I was being cautious in trying to figure it all out. He, on the other hand, was throwing his arms open wide, and welcoming me into his world without reservation.

What did it all mean? Did I dare trust him? Did I dare let my feelings of friendship and fascination develop into more? I was unsure of myself and the world around me.

The rest of the weekend passed in a blur, but I sensed that that moment was of great significance to José. Was I missing something, or was this really a sign from God? Should I allow myself to explore this relationship further, or should I close the book on it and look elsewhere? For the moment, I did not know. I prayed to God and hoped that time would tell.

CHAPTER 5

When we returned to Mexico City, I threw myself into my studies. I spent hours in the library of the Museum of Anthropology, reading about Mexico's history. I also took the opportunity to visit the Wycliffe Institute as often as possible. An elderly missionary named Betty invited me to go to the village with her for a few days.

We loaded her Jeep with supplies and took off one Friday morning. She drove down a sunny road, which descended from the plateau to a tropical area with lush vegetation and a strong smell of humus.

Conditions in the village were primitive. Lacking running water and electricity, the villagers lived a sparse existence and had little contact with the outside world. Their simple mud houses were scattered among the trees and bushes on a hillside. There were no public buildings and no school.

"None of the people speaks Spanish," said Betty. "My co-worker, Mary, and I have spent the last twenty-five years living here and translating the Bible."

"How long did it take you to learn the language?" I wanted to know.

"It took a few years because there were no written materials, and each language has its own sounds, which one must first identify. Fortunately when we first came, we knew of a young man who spoke a little Spanish, so he helped introduce us to the villagers."

"How did they react when you first came?"

"Suspicious. They couldn't understand what we were doing here. They kept asking us if we were sisters, and when we told them we weren't related, they decided we were lesbians."

"What? You?"

"Well, of course we're not! But how do you explain that to people, once the rumor has gotten around? We've just had to live here with our windows open and let them watch our every move. I'm a nurse, so I've been able to help some of them when they were really sick, and the children are always coming by with their scrapes and bruises. That is what finally made them accept us. They don't bother us any more. We have written a couple of primers and have started to teach the children to read in our home. They like that."

Betty's and Mary's hut was just like everyone else's, but they were foreigners, and they wore store-bought, cotton dresses. Their kitchen implements were the same as the villagers', except they disinfected their raw vegetables before eating them. In the kitchen was a huge window that they opened whenever they woke up in the morning, and the village children soon arrived to watch the day's goings-on.

I started to observe Betty and Mary through the eyes of the children. As soon as the women got up, they went to a barrel of water, poured some into a little bowl, and put some on their faces and hands. Then they took some more water and put it in a pot on the fire. When it was steaming, they put the bowl on the stone floor. Then they went to another bowl of water that had food floating in it, and they ate some. As soon as they finished that, they went back to the washing bowl and dipped their fingers in the water again.

Then they prepared another bowl of water and put fruit and vegetables in it. They took a small bottle and let a few drops of liquid fall into the bowl of water. They left the bowl there for hours. Then they went to the bowl of steamed water to see if it had cooled off enough to drink. They poured some into a glass and sat down at the table to meditate on a book. At noon, they got up and washed again before eating. They bowed to pray, ate, and got up to wash again.

After lunch, they put more water in a bowl, sprinkled a powder in it, and put their clothes in it to soak. They didn't go down to the river to wash their clothes by slapping them on the stones and rinsing them in the running water, as did the other women in the village. They didn't go down to the river to bathe, either. They just stayed in their house, bowing and washing, and moving a stick on a piece of paper all day.

In the evening, they went to the little bowl of water one more time and put some on their faces. Then they took a colored stick, massaged it around inside their mouths, and spit out froth. They put some more water in their mouths and spat that out too. Then they smiled, said goodbye to the children, and closed the big window till the next morning. The children learned a lot about this strange water-religion and went home to tell their parents all about it.

Eventually, however, Betty's and Mary's literacy work would be life changing for the tribe. Learning to read would integrate them into the rest of the Mexican culture, and it would give them an opportunity to read the story of Jesus for themselves.

I was glad for the opportunity to witness firsthand what a Wycliffe translator's life was like, but I decided I wasn't cut out for that kind of work. Rather than spend the next few years learning an obscure language, I was eager to return to the bustle of the city and communicate with the Indian people who already spoke Spanish.

My university was within thirty minutes' walking distance. I had on leather walking shoes with high heels that *clip-clopped* on the pavement, and a blue tartan miniskirt and yellow sweater that reflected brightly in the store windows as I walked by. Many of the stores contained beautiful Mexican silver, and the pavement was partially shaded by enormous palm trees. It was September, and the sun shone brightly.

Being a morning person, I was always in a good mood on the way to school. I was excited to be in a foreign country all by myself, studying new subjects and making new friends. I always looked forward to each new day as a brand-new adventure, and I loved meeting new people along the way.

During the day, I went to classes, and at night, I either studied or went to church. After dark, the city looked strangely eerie, with little, bright lights shining everywhere. Each driver adorned the inside of his bus or taxi with gaudy pictures of the Virgin of Guadalupe, cheap furry toys made in Korea, and suggestive plastic women with big breasts. The streets were cluttered with booths selling everything from chewing gum to shoe polish, from blankets to hot, spicy soup. The smells of food cooking was overpowering and mysterious.

One Saturday night, José took me to the Zocalo market in the center of town. It was filled with wooden tables and benches where one could eat thin Mexican steaks and handmade corn tortillas. He embarrassed me by contracting a band of mariachis to sing to me as we ate, and then we took a romantic stroll through the Zocalo Park. We sat down on one of the white, wrought-iron benches and laughed and talked.

I was losing myself in a wonderful world of mystery and magic, a romantic world where men serenaded women, bought them roses, and spoke in flowery terms of their undying love and devotion. José was telling me how lovely I was, how much he liked being with me, and how good I made him feel. A flower vendor selling long-stem roses walked by. José bought one, and as we passed a large, white statue in the park, he whisked around, handed me the rose, and kissed me.

As I lay in my bed that night, I wondered if I had finally found the romance that I had been looking for. I had yearned for years to find someone who would love me and want me for who I was, and not just for what I could do. José had no way of gauging just where I stood academically, and he seemed to accept me just as I was. And he did a lot more than just accept me. He wanted me. He wanted me very badly. He wanted me more than anyone had ever wanted me before.

I needed so much to be wanted. To belong. To be loved. Was it possible that God was answering my prayers and my years of loneliness and heartache? I had told Him I was ready to fall in love with someone who was romantic and fun! Could this finally be it?

CHAPTER 6

The following morning, it was time to pick up my student visa. I stood in line at the government office. When my turn came, the official at the window lowered his voice.

"I'm afraid we cannot give you back your passport, Señorita," he said gravely.

"Why not?" I asked, in a panic.

"Because the Mexican government is filing suit against you."

I was stunned. "A suit? For what?" I asked.

"For falsification of documents," the official answered.

I was aghast. I couldn't believe this was happening to me. Visions of years in a Mexican jail flashed before my eyes.

"Step this way, please. You need to talk to the boss in his private office."

We went down several corridors, up the elevator, and finally reached the boss's office. It was quiet, secluded, and comfortably decorated. There sat a man with a mustache, rocking in a big, executive chair. He was about thirty-five, and chubby, with a long-sleeved shirt and tie.

"Sit down, Señorita," he motioned, in a very serious tone. "We have a big problem here."

I listened, perplexed.

"The Mexican government has drawn up these papers," he said, waving two, typed, legal sheets at me, "and is filing suit against you. I need you to sign here at the bottom."

He pointed his finger at the spot where I was to sign my life away.

"With all due respect," I stammered, "there must be some mistake here. I haven't falsified any documents. I'm just a student sent here by my university to study the Spanish language."

"Oh, yes. You have falsified your documents. We have proof. Please sign."

"May I read the papers first?" I asked.

"Of course," he said, sitting back down and waving his hand as if to say that I was wasting my time. He probably didn't expect me to understand the long legalese in which the document was drafted.

"This statement is not true, sir," I said. "Where is the proof that you refer to?"

"Right here!" he said, slapping down the original visa application that the female employee at the Mexican consulate in London had filled out by hand.

He opened the booklet dramatically and pointed in disgust to her handwritten answers.

"You can see here that the answers are all typewritten, and yet, here you have handwritten your answers in pen. This is considered falsification of government documents."

"That's not my handwriting. I didn't fill that out," I said, in a wave of relief. "The lady at the consulate in London wrote in the booklet, and then when I entered the country, an official at the airport typed over the answers."

I was sure that my explanation would resolve the matter instantly, but the man was not to be moved.

"These are your documents, Señorita, and this visa application of yours has both handwritten and typed answers. This is just not acceptable to the Mexican government. We have to sue you."

"Please, sir," I begged. "This is all a big mistake. It's just as I told you; I didn't do it. Is there anything I can do to resolve this problem?" I pleaded.

He held up his hand and rubbed his thumb against his next two fingers. Unbeknownst to me, he was fishing for a bribe.

"You mean there's going to be a fine? But sir, I'm a student on a limited budget. I don't have any money, and I didn't do anything wrong. Is there any way you can help me?"

He leaned back and started rocking in his chair, as if deep in thought. Idly, he opened my passport and gazed at it.

"This is a really pretty picture of you," he said, looking me in the eye intently.

"Thank you." I blushed and waited for him to return to the subject at hand.

"You know, Señorita, maybe I can help you."

"Oh?" I said, leaning forward in anticipation.

"Yes. I get off at seven on Friday evening. Maybe if you meet me at the back door, I might be able to give you back your passport and drop the whole thing."

Suddenly, it began to dawn on me what he was implying. He had trumped up the whole thing just to get me in his office and seduce me.

"Let me think about it," I said sheepishly. All I wanted to do was to get out of there as quickly as possible. I didn't care about my passport anymore. I just wanted to be out on the street, free again.

"Why are you crying?" asked my landlady when she came home that night.

I told her the whole awful story.

"Wipe your tears, you silly girl. That's why you have a British consulate here in Mexico City. I will personally call down there tomorrow and get you an interview with the consul himself. He will make sure you get all your papers back in order.

The consul assigned me the consulate lawyer, and after three more mornings of missed classes, my passport and visa were unceremoniously returned to me. The offending individual was given a pretend slap on the hand, and business in the Mexican government offices continued on as usual.

I didn't realize at the time how this most sordid, unpleasant incident would be the key to my deliverance later on in my stay.

CHAPTER 7

José started to come into town more often, just to see me. It took him several hours each way, so he would come straight from school, spend the night at his parents' apartment, and leave again early the next morning. He would often be at my place until late into the night.

The weekends were the most fun, because he liked the simple people in the country and took me to visit the church where he preached.

"I've been working with the Indians for several years now. First, as a teacher, I helped bring electricity to some remote villages. Now, as a preacher, I go to a little church way out in the mountains and preach. Even though the people have their own language, they are close enough to civilization that they all speak some Spanish. I make my sermons really down-to-earth, and the people seem to like me."

He made a point of going to somebody's home after each service. Not wanting them to go to any expense on his behalf, he made each visit spontaneous. He ate whatever they gave him, and since in Mexico, accepting people's food means accepting them, he was a great hit. He always licked his fingers and praised the cooking, which quickly put the women on his side. He talked about current events with the men and petted the children, so everyone liked him and eagerly awaited his return.

"I'm so pleased that you enjoy going with me to the villages," José told me one day. "You act naturally and blend in right away, despite the simplicity of their lifestyle. That means a lot to me, because I love being with them. I have always dreamed of having a companion who loved the indigenous people and was willing to leave the glamour of city life to minister to them, but I have never found anyone like you. You are obviously so superior and classy, and yet you are so friendly. You seem to want to be here."

"I've always wanted to be a missionary to the Indians in Latin America," I said.

"Well, I am one, and since that is your desire, I want you to come to my grandparents' village and meet my grandparents. I call them Abuelito and Abuelita. They live just a few miles outside of my town of San Martín. If you like the Indian people, you'll love my grandparents!"

So one weekend, we took a bus up a serpentine road toward Morelia. The mountain slopes were lush with grass and pine trees. Cottages clung to the hillsides, and a thin film of clouds marred the otherwise clear blue sky.

We drove through Toluca, a sprawling industrial town. The bus took us down a wide boulevard, past factory after factory surrounded by iron bars, and then stopped in the giant, concrete terminal for passengers to get on and off. I stared through the wire fence, across a field of rubble and trash, to the market in the distance. It seemed so strange and foreign to be there. I wondered what San Martín would be like.

After Toluca, the road narrowed, and we rode across a plateau with cornfields, aloe-vera cactus plants, and scattered farmhouses. Several hours later, the bus started up a small hill, and I saw a sign that read SAN MARTÍN.

José helped me down the steep steps of the bus at the main square. There was a big central plaza, surrounded by low buildings. They were simply built, with big, brown wooden beams, bright red Spanish tile roofs, and steel burglar bars in the tiny windows. All the houses were painted with white limestone, which gave them a pristine appearance. Along one end of the square was an arcade with a barber and a pharmacy open to the pedestrian traffic.

The people in San Martín were obviously agrarian folks. Many of the Indian men were dressed as ranchers in shoddy pants, dusty shoes, and big cowboy hats. Some had things to do, while others just stood around in clusters, smoking and watching the passersby.

"Sometimes when the Catholics have their fiestas," said José, "pilgrims walk through San Martín on their way to the Basilica of the Virgin of Guadalupe in Mexico City. They often stop here for the night and just sleep on the pavement. Sometimes they get drunk and start brawls, and it's not unusual for there to be a shooting."

Most of the women were Indian too. They wore brightly colored clothing, bought cheaply at the local markets. Many had long, black silky hair woven neatly into braids. Some carried their babies in a traditional pink or gray shawl across their shoulders. A row of them sat on the ground beside cauldrons of spicy food, which they sold to the passersby.

José took my elbow and led me across the square to the market building. As we passed the women sitting on the ground, a scruffy dog ran by and stepped accidentally into one of the women's cauldrons of brown "mole" sauce. Without missing a beat, the woman grabbed the dog's hind leg and squeezed the sauce right back into the cauldron.

Inside the market were open-air stalls displaying every kind of produce, meat, canned goods, baskets, toys, and clothes. In one of the candy stalls, a middle-aged woman, wearing her hair tied back with a thick piece of pink wool, stood on a crate. She was bending over, rummaging through an old cardboard box.

"Señora Jovita," José said, leading me up to her stand. "I need two thick milk shakes with eggs and cocoa powder in them!" Señora Jovita jumped to attention, rinsing her blender before she began.

"Two shakes coming up, Señor Profesór!" she said, busying herself with her latest order.

"Mmmm, Señora Jovita! This is delicious!" José gurgled. "Nobody in the world makes as good a milk shake as you do! That's why I'm so strong, because your shakes give me energy!"

Señora Jovita laughed in embarrassment.

"Oh, get along with you, Profesór. I know you are just flattering me, but tell me, who is the Señorita?"

"This is Helenita. I've brought her to San Martín, so she can see where I live."

"Well, we're very honored to have you, Señorita. Come to my milk shake stand any time you want."

We left Señora Jovita and made our way through the market to a fruit stand, tended by a spotlessly clean Indian woman with a fresh-scrubbed face.

"This is Helenita, Aunt Socorro," José said, as I reached out to shake her cold hand over the pile of bananas.

Aunt Socorro started to laugh in embarrassment, covering her mouth with her weather-reddened hand.

"She's pretty, José. Is she an American?"

"No, Aunt Socorro. She's from England."

"England? Do you have to take a boat to get to England?"

"It's on the other side of the world," I volunteered, "but I came here by plane."

"Oh," sighed Aunt Socorro, impressed. "Well, we're glad to have you. Come by our house in the village. The grandparents would love to meet you."

"Thanks. I will," I said.

"Well, we have to run," said José. "Bye, Aunt Socorro. We'll see you later!"

"All right, José, thanks for stopping by, Señorita. It's an honor for me to meet you."

José took my elbow and led me down a rough, cobbled street, past more decorated white buildings, down toward one of the barrios. At the bottom of the hill, the cobbles came to an abrupt end, and the orange dirt road was filled with puddles. Arranged in higgledy-piggledy fashion was a plethora of concrete houses in various stages of construction. Most were still unpainted, and the rooftops were randomly crisscrossed with clotheslines, where women hung their hand-washed clothes to dry.

"This house is mine," said José, pulling out his key and heading toward a dark, wooden door. "It is a rustic cottage really, but it suits me just fine."

He pushed open the door, and we walked from one empty room to another. The dusty walls were several feet thick, and in the empty kitchen was an old-fashioned stone stove. At the end of the concrete corridor was an open patio with a stone washstand and a single water spigot. To the side of the patio was one last room, kept under lock and key.

"This is where I stay," José said. "Come in."

We stepped out of the sunlight and into a modest room about twelve feet by twelve feet. In it was a sofa bed; a table; a chair; and a simple, wooden clothes closet. An intricately woven, straw cowboy hat hung on a nail in the wall.

He reached out and put it on, turning to me with a big smile.

"See, Helenita. This is my world. I take a bus out to a village down the road, where I'm the vice principal in a rural elementary school. The people are very poor. I helped bring roads and electricity to them a few years ago. I really feel as if I'm doing something useful here. The area is so backward. I want to help."

From there, we took a cheap cab down a red-mud road in the opposite direction to visit his grandparents' village. On either side of the road, piles of white rock fences and miles of dark green cactus plants stuck up into a bright blue sky. Occasionally, we passed a barefooted urchin leading the family donkey down to the well to refill the tin cans with water.

The cab stopped to let us off, right outside a mud hut. Two older men were sitting on the stone wall outside, drinking pulque, a beer made from local cactus plants.

"Hola, José! What brings you here?" said the younger of the two men. He was in his forties, wearing a white hat, a tattered shirt, and earth-soiled pants.

"Buenos días, Uncle Chucho! I've brought someone to meet you! Buenos días, Abuelito," he said respectfully, bending down to kiss the back of the older man's hand. "How's Abuelita doing?"

"She's in there making tortillas, hijito. Hey, woman, come out here and greet your guests!" he yelled, turning to hobble toward the kitchen.

Out of the kitchen door stepped a short, white-haired old woman with neat, long braids; a thick gray skirt; and a bright red, checkered apron. Despite her age, she was trim and pretty. She blinked, unused to the brightness of the sun.

"Hola, José," she said, her lips widening in a big smile, revealing a row of perfect white teeth and a love only a grandmother can have.

José stepped forward and kissed her tenderly on the forehead.

"I've brought Helenita to taste some of your delicious tortillas, Abuelita."

"Well, come on in, come on in!" said the brown-skinned little grandmother. "I'll send one of the little ones to the corner store to buy a couple of Coca Colas. We're so honored to meet you, Helenita. We were just getting ready for lunch. Come sit down." I was already in love with her. She was so warm, so enthusiastic!

I shook everyone's hand and followed Abuelita into the dimly lit kitchen. In the middle of the hut was a table covered with a plastic tablecloth and surrounded by rustic chairs. All kinds of kitchen implements hung from the rafters that supported the straw roof, and some earthenware bowls were stacked on the dirt floor. Hot cinders and a tortilla pan sat on the stone stove. Another aunt sat by the stove, patting the tortillas and turning them over so they would cook without burning.

"Did you hear of the latest wreck?" asked Uncle Chucho. "Buses are always falling off a cliff near town," he told me, by way of explanation. "One of the most popular topics people discuss around here is how it happened, how many died, and how many were taken to the local hospital!"

"No, I didn't," said the grandfather, "but one of our neighbors was in a wreck down there a few years ago and had to have surgery. She had stomach pains for years after that. She went back in to see the doctor last week, and when they x-rayed her stomach, they found a pair of scissors still in there from the surgery!"

"That's typical," said Abuelita. "I just hope I never have to go into a hospital. Once they start cutting you open, you never know what's going to happen!"

They made me feel very welcome and very comfortable among them. Abuelita laughed cheerfully and plied me with roast cacti, bacon and beans, and lots and lots of tortillas. Despite her age and primitive surroundings, she talked as freely as any liberated woman. Her husband pretended to be gruff and macho with her, but I could tell that he was camouflaging a sweet and tender love.

"Your grandparents are great!" I told José on the way back to Mexico City in the bus that night. I had finally met the Indians in the mountains with whom I had for so long wanted to live, and I loved being with them. José squeezed my hand affectionately, and we leaned our seats back for the long ride back to the city.

CHAPTER 8

José was street smart. Nimble and alert, he took pride in protecting me from the crowds on the pavements and in the buses. He would grab me by the hand, hold me by the elbow, or put his arm around me, and skillfully maneuver us through the crowds. I loved his decisiveness and felt sheltered from the crowds by his large, strong body.

I wondered if my initial misgivings about him had been real, or if I had just been too overwhelmed by the evening of Madeleine's conversion. Everything I saw about him seemed genuine, even childlike. He took me rowing on the lake or to feed the animals in the zoo. He enjoyed making fresh-squeezed orange juice or helping a child up the stairs. He was affectionate, spontaneous, and fun loving.

José never worried about anything. He saw no obstacles to our relationship, only a future full of happiness and promise. When he took me to meet his parents for the first time,

I only hoped that they would see it the same way. I was delighted to be in love, but deep down I had some lingering doubts. Just from meeting his grandparents, I knew that we were economically, and culturally, worlds apart.

"I've waited this long to introduce you to my parents because I wanted to be sure of our relationship. My mother is a very smart woman. She can see through everything. She may not immediately agree that we belong together, but I will talk her into it. You'll see."

José's parents lived in the concrete jungle behind a giant supermarket. Thousands of cars, buses, and taxicabs in various states of disrepair streamed along the heavily trafficked artery, spewing pollution into the air. Every once in a while, an angry driver would cross lanes, honk, or shake a provocative fist. Traffic lights turned green and red, as millions jostled and pushed their way down crowded sidewalks and jumped on and off already overloaded buses.

"My parents came from the village twenty-five years ago," he explained. "They didn't even own a pair of shoes, but they sold lemons to the passersby. Eventually they saved up enough money to open their own little produce shop and raise a family. I really admire them, because so many other poor people just give up and go begging, but they didn't. I received a college education, and so did several of my brothers and sisters. Now that we are older, we all pitch in and help them pay their bills."

We were in a blue-collar neighborhood full of identical apartment buildings of cinder block and faded paint. Music blared from the open windows. Children and dogs had long since worn out any remnants of grass. The rancid smell of the slaughterhouse blew in from across the railway tracks, and occasionally an article of clothing hung from the windows to dry.

The iron gate to their building was open. We made our way up a dingy flight of stairs and knocked on the first door.

"Who is it?" said a low voice from within.

"Open up! I'm home!" replied José.

Cries of delight could be heard from within. The bolt was pulled away, and the door opened into a well-lighted hallway. We stepped inside.

José immediately hugged first one and then another family member. Except for him, they all lived together in this tight little apartment, and his arrival seemed to cause quite a stir.

"This is Helenita," José beamed, and I politely stretched out my hand as the introductions were made. José's father was a short man, slightly bald, with a big grin, showing some loose false teeth. His mother had long, gray pigtails, curly eyelashes, and a shy smile. His chubby sisters grinned shyly, and his brothers respectfully shook my hand.

It was supper time. A huge table filled the whole living room, barely allowing me to squeeze through and sit down. The walls were painted in shocking pink, and on the floor was a shaggy, pink rug. José, his father, his brothers, and I were seated at the table, while his mother and sisters stood in the kitchen, warming the tortillas. José was the life of the party; he seemed to have everyone in stitches all the time.

I kept hoping that his mother and sisters would join us at the table. I didn't know that it was the Mexican custom for women to stand and serve, while the men and the visitors ate. They chatted happily in the kitchen, reappearing only to take our empty plates away and bring on more goodies.

"Well, what did your mother say?" I asked José, when he and I were back on the street together.

"She says it's never going to work. She says we're too different. She says we're from two different cultures, and

I'll never be able to give you the kind of lifestyle you're accustomed to. I tried to explain to her, but you know how mothers are!"

"Well, she's right, you know. We are from completely different worlds. You don't know anything about my background, and it is very different from yours."

"So? We're both Christians. We both want to work as missionaries among the Indians. We get along great, and we have a good time. I don't see a problem. I told my parents that. My mother just worries. I told her you're not like the others. I can't get a Mexican girl to go out to the village with me. I can't get any girl from our city church to go out to the country churches with me. They all want fancy boyfriends with fancy cars!"

He was right. Just that week in the restroom at the city church I had heard the girls talking.

"Have you seen Manuel's new convertible?" one had said.

"No, but I wouldn't be seen dead with Rigoberto! He comes to church by bus, and he always wears that old leather jacket!"

I was torn. On the one hand, I understood what José's mother was saying; on the other hand, I saw José's point too. We did have a lot in common, and since my dream was to work among the Indians in South America, money just didn't seem to be that important.

I wished I could talk to Howard Klassen at the Wycliffe Institute about my dilemma. He seemed as if he was an understanding sort of person, and I almost spoke up that following Friday night as I sat with him and his wife in the quiet of their lovely den. But for some reason, I held back. I was embarrassed and afraid.

Afraid that if I spoke up, they might tell me what a bad idea it was. Afraid that if I asked their opinion, they might try to talk sense to me, and I wasn't sure I wanted to hear reason. José was so romantic and such fun to be with. I was twenty-two years old, and time was slipping by. What if I never had another opportunity to fall in love?

After all, José wanted me. He wanted me more than anyone I had ever known. He lavished me with praise, flowers, and romantic words. He took me on excursions and opened his world to me without reserve. He made me feel special and beautiful, and he treated me like a queen.

I had wanted romance, and his love and attention were all around me. I had wanted fun, and he was always ready to have a good time. I had wanted someone who loved the poor in the Third World, and he lived among them. I had wanted a missionary, and he preached enthusiastically in the villages. I had wanted to be with the South American Indians, and he worked among them with ease and commitment.

I had wanted someone who loved me for who I was, without looking at my achievements and credentials; to him they were meaningless. I had wanted someone who thought I was pretty; he called me his little doll. I had wanted someone who was intelligent, but not proud; his wit and good humor constantly amazed me. He was so genuine, so unassuming. He seemed to be everything I had wished for.

And so it was when he appeared with twenty-four plump red roses and fell on one knee and asked me to marry him. I could think of no objections, and said "yes."

I still had to go to Belgium for eight months and then back to Scotland for my final year. I promised that after I graduated, I would return to marry him—on one condition: he had to come to London to ask for my hand.

CHAPTER 9

It was almost time to leave Mexico City and return to London. I was due in Belgium in a week for the second half of my year abroad. My suitcases and boxes were all by the door. I had spent every last peso on souvenirs, and I would be back in England in a matter of hours. Since my landlady was going out of town, José invited me to stay with his family my last night in Mexico City.

I packed my bags and was saying my goodbyes, when the doorbell rang.

"Ready to go, Princess?"

José enthusiastically helped me with my luggage. We had to make two trips in the elevator.

"Wait in the lobby, Helena. I'll run out and hail a taxi. It's raining."

I sat on my suitcase, thinking back over my six-month stay in Mexico City. It had been so colorful, and I was sad that it was over. I had made many friends in the church and among José's family. One of the ladies in the church had even written a poem about me, calling me "Christ's little traveler." I would miss them all, especially the Abuelitos and the girls at the church. I wondered whether they believed that I would really return to marry José.

We had walked hand in hand along the Reforma Avenue on our last night together.

"Time flies, Helenita," he had said. "Before long you'll be back, and we'll have a glorious wedding at the church here. We'll invite everyone, even the poor little old ladies who don't get invited to any fancy weddings. You'll be the most gorgeous bride with your light brown hair and your green eyes covered mysteriously with a veil. Then I'll lift it and look into your lovely, fair face. I'll be so proud to kiss you in front of everyone.

"You are the best thing that's ever happened to me. I have dreamed of you all my life. We will be missionaries among the Indians, and we will be so happy together. We'll have at least five children, and you'll be a wonderful mother, you'll see. . . ."

Suddenly, I realized I had been day-dreaming, and I wondered what was taking José so long. Finally, he ran into the building, breathless.

"It's pouring out there, and all the taxis were taken. I've got one now, and he'll give us a good price. Go on out. I'll get the suitcases."

I covered my head with my Mexican shawl and crawled quickly into the back of the taxi. The windshield wipers were moving hypnotically from side to side. Through the raindrops, I could see the blurred lights of the city. Cars were driving erratically, people were running for shelter, and the traffic was bumper to bumper.

José loaded my luggage, and we were on our way. As usual, he chatted with the driver and used the opportunity to tell him about Christ. Eventually we passed the slaughterhouse.

"Here it is. Just turn in on the left, and stop by the telephone kiosk," José said, as we approached his parents' apartment complex. The rain was still pouring down. I waited in the car while José ran in to alert his family. His brothers came out to help with the luggage.

"Run in, Helenita! We'll get the bags!" José said. I jumped across the gushing water in the gutter and ran for the building, covering my head with the shawl. The rest of the family was inside, waiting to greet me.

"I'm drenched! Let me hang the shawl out to dry," I said. The men came running in, loaded down with my bags.

"That's it! I think we got it all, and he did give us a good price."

"I'll just go in the bathroom and comb my hair," I said. "It's dripping wet. Let me . . . Oh, no! Where did I put my handbag? It's not here, and I don't remember . . . I put it down by my feet in the taxi. Run and catch him before he leaves!"

The men rushed out in the rain. It was too late. He had already gone.

"Now what?" My brain was numb. I thought I was going to collapse. My knees wanted to give out under me. My handbag containing my passport, my airline ticket to New York, and from New York to London, my diary, my student identification, my makeup, and I couldn't even remember what else—it was all in my handbag, and it was gone!

Blindly, I wished for a miracle. Some incredible occurrence would get me on that plane; I knew it would. This couldn't be happening to me. I couldn't even picture not being on that plane in the morning.

"What can we do?" I pleaded. José's brother, Gilberto, called the radio and television stations and asked them to put on an announcement.

"Maybe the driver will hear about it and come right back to deliver my purse," I said.

"No way! Not in Mexico!" answered José's brother, Epifanio. "Anyone who finds the purse will take the money and throw the purse away. People don't like to turn in missing property for fear of being accused of stealing thousands. Nobody could ever prove what was really in the purse; it would be your word against theirs, and they don't want to take that risk."

My hopes were still high, but my reasoning powers seemed to be in slow motion. I could not accept this. It was more than I could handle. I was supposed to be going to the other side of the world in the morning, and now my handbag was gone!

No driver came by; no phone call relieved me from my misery. My mind grasped helplessly for a solution. If I could have gotten it back by sheer nervous energy, it would have been there.

I slept fitfully, tossing and turning. Every once in a while, I would look at my bed stand to see if my handbag had miraculously appeared, but to no avail. My alarm was set for 6:00; all my things were neatly lined up, ready to go; everything was set—but my bag was still missing.

The alarm startled me precisely at 6:00. Nothing had changed. The horrible truth was becoming very clear. My parents were there, and I was here. The plane was leaving, and I was not going to be on it. There was no miracle. There was no handbag. So there would be no flight. I couldn't fly without a ticket, and I couldn't leave without a passport!

I decided I would be brave. I would get dressed and go out and see what I could do to resolve this mess. By the end of the business day I would have an alternative plan, so I could call my parents before they started driving for the airport. They would panic if I weren't there when they arrived.

At the same time, I couldn't just call them up in London and say, "Hello Mummy! Hello Daddy! I'm still in Mexico. I have no passport, I have no ticket, I have no money, and I don't know if I'll ever get out of here, but I'm fine. Don't worry!" No, I couldn't do that. I would have to give them an alternative arrival date.

At 9:00 sharp, I was at the airline office. The security guard unlocked the door, and I rushed in.

"I have a reservation for the 9:45 flight to New York, Señorita," I blurted out to the reservationist. "But my ticket is gone! Can you give me a refund?"

"We can give you a refund, of course, but you'll have to fill out these forms and mail them to our New York office. They will send you a check in approximately ninety days."

"Ninety days? But I don't have any money! I can't make an alternate reservation if I don't get the refund right away!"

"I'm sorry, Señorita. It's company policy. There's nothing I can do."

I walked out of the agency defeated. José and his mother were with me.

"Now what?" I asked, looking at them in a panic. José's mother had put on her black skirt, pink blouse, and gray shawl. She was standing on the pavement, her arm in José's.

"You can stay with us for a few days," she said kindly. "God will provide."

She always said that. It didn't matter what the crisis was, she was always calm, and somehow, some way, God always did provide. There was a sweet strength about her. She didn't get flustered in any situation. Her faith was unshakable, and she was always very gracious to me. She and José's father had spent the night praying. She knew a solution would be forthcoming.

"Let's go to the British consulate and see what they can do to give me an alternate passport. I don't know how that will happen, though, since I have absolutely no documentation to prove who I am!"

The British guard saluted stiffly as we made our way through the iron gate and up the stairs into the impressive lobby. I had been there several times before in pursuit of my confiscated passport, so I knew exactly where to go.

"Mr. Jones will see you now," said his petite, English secretary. I pushed the door open, and made my way over the enormous red Turkish carpet to Mr. Jones' grandiose desk.

"Hello, Helen. So we meet again. What can I do for you this time?"

All of a sudden I recognized my miracle. Had I not been accused of falsifying my documents earlier in my stay, I never would have come to the British consulate, and I never would have met Mr. Jones. Then, nobody would have known who I was, or even that I was a British citizen, and I would have had no way of proving it either!

Mr. Jones listened attentively to my tale of woe.

"The British government can certainly repatriate you, but it will cost a lot more than your original fare."

"How much more?" I asked.

"About three times as much," he replied. "Furthermore," he said, pushing himself slowly away from his desk and picking up his gold pen, "we can only issue you a temporary passport if your plane refuels in Bermuda. There are no direct flights to London from here, and you cannot stop in any non-British territory."

My heart sank.

"What if she can come up with the money for a student ticket," José asked, "would you still give her the temporary passport?"

"Most certainly. If you can get a ticket via Bermuda, we can certainly issue you the papers."

"I just had an idea!" I said. "My friend Keith, the other student here from Edinburgh, had a lot of problems with his grant money, so he had his full year's stipend sent to Mexico. I haven't kept in touch with him, but I have his phone number. Maybe I could call him for a loan as soon as we leave here."

Keith was my only hope. Fortunately, he said he had the money and agreed to make me a short-term loan. Now all I had to do was find a flight that refueled in Bermuda.

José, his mother, and I walked along Reforma Avenue from one airline office to another. Finally, just before closing time late that afternoon, British Airways agreed to sell me a ticket via Bermuda for a student price, providing I could bring proof from the University in Mexico City that I had been a student there.

I ran to the public telephone shop. The clerk allotted me a booth and dialed the number for me. I could hear the familiar, quick double-ring, and immediately I could picture my hallway back home. It was the middle of the night in London now. Hardly a civilized time to call, but I wanted to catch my parents before they left for the airport to pick me up.

"It's me, Helen!" I yelled into the receiver.

"Helen? What's going on?" My father's confused voice reverberated across the line, and I could hear my mother and my younger sister, Lucy, who was home from university, talking heatedly in the background. I had obviously caused quite a commotion.

"I'm still in Mexico City. I missed my flight."

"What happened? Are you all right?" My father was most concerned.

"I'm fine. I'll tell you all about it when I get there. It's too expensive to talk long distance. I'll be arriving next Sunday morning at Heathrow Airport at 8:55 A.M. on British Airways via Bermuda"

"But are you all right?"

"Yes, I'm fine. Everything's fine. I have to go. I'll see you next Sunday."

I would tell them the details when I got home. In the meantime, I had a glorious bonus week to spend with José, just having fun!

CHAPTER 10

W hat on earth happened to you?" my parents inquired, as I sat on the soft leather seat in the back of my father's Rover.

"I lost my handbag with everything in it, so I couldn't come home right away," I told them. "Now I have to go all the way to Scotland to get a new student card, or they will not allow me to register in Belgium. I'm probably going to be late to class in Mons."

My travel insurance reimbursed me some money, and I eventually got a refund for my ticket from Mexico to New York, but the flight from New York to London had been a nonrefundable charter. I would just have to be frugal with my grant money so I could repay Keith everything I owed him.

We lived in a quiet suburb of London. My father was a traveling businessman, my mother a fashion designer. Both were well educated and artistic. Our home was tastefully decorated, with beautifully manicured rose bushes in front and back.

My room overlooked the large lawn and shrubbery in the back. While I was repacking my luggage one afternoon, my mother came into the bedroom. She sat down on the bed and watched me.

"Mummy," I said hesitantly, "I met someone in Mexico. He's a teacher, and he wants to marry me."

My mother took it with a grain of salt. After all, I had come back. With a long stay in Belgium, then one more year of school back in Edinburgh, she figured I had plenty of time to become disillusioned.

"Surely you wouldn't want to live in such a primitive place as Mexico, would you?" she asked.

"Mexico City isn't primitive! It's a huge, modern city," I protested. But deep down, it was true. I had to admit that I didn't really like the city. It felt so alien. Even though it was a modern city, I had never felt totally comfortable there.

But then I thought about José's smile, the white houses shining in the sun in San Martín, the crisp skies and towering mountains, the peasant women with their long pigtails. Yes, that was Latin America. That was where I had been called to go, and marrying José would be a step in the right direction.

I made a quick trip to Edinburgh and then crossed the English channel on a large ferry, arriving in Mons exactly one week late.

My living arrangements couldn't have been more perfect. My room was in a quaint, old house directly opposite the university. Madame Lemaire, my stately old landlady, was a coal-miner's widow. Her prim little parlor was filled with doilies, china, cut glass, and statuettes. On the richly papered walls were black-and-white photos of her departed husband, and group pictures of his coal-mining friends.

Madame Lemaire remembered not only the second World War, but also the First. Sipping her lonely aperitif as the clock struck five every afternoon, a tear trickled down her ruddy face, rolled under her gold-rimmed glasses, and plopped down onto her lace apron.

As she was unable to climb the stairs, she rented her beautifully decorated upstairs bedroom and huge, old-fashioned bathroom with a porcelain tub in the middle of an antique linoleum floor, to me.

In the silent cocoon of Madame Lemaire's abode, I found time to pray and be alone. I needed to reflect about my stay in Mexico and start preparing myself to return there. I bought a French Bible and started to pray for wisdom. Wisdom, above all things, was to be sought-after and cherished, said the Old Testament writer of the Book of Proverbs. "Charm is deceitful, and beauty is vain, But a woman who fears the Lord, she shall be praised" (Prov. 31:30 NKJV).

José sent me romantic cards and wrote lengthy letters almost every other day. It felt wonderful to be loved. I kept remembering his beaming smile, the decisiveness with which he leapt in and out of the busy city traffic, and the disarming look in his eyes when he gazed into mine and asked me to marry him. Now I had a future to look forward to with him, and I wanted to spend time alone, getting ready.

My room was cozy. The bed was covered in a heavy, green taffeta bedspread. There was a little table for me to sit by and carpet mats for me to kneel on. The silence was beautiful, and the presence of God was very real. I wanted, above all, for Him to guide my life and prepare me to become a missionary in Latin America.

For my dissertation in French, I decided to study the mistakes interpreters make and to classify them into categories. There was no literature on the subject, so it presented the kind of pioneer challenge I enjoyed.

On several occasions, I taped a speaker and a whole row of interpreters, then sat in my bedroom listening to each one's tape, logging each mistake, and then looking for patterns in their errors. Then I counted the number of incidents of each error and classified them by order of occurrence. It was a project that kept me occupied for months.

I was in my interpreting booth one day when I heard a commotion in the booth next to mine. I got up to look. When I opened the door to the other booth, it was dark. I turned on the light and saw a man desperately pawing the floor.

"What's the matter?" I asked.

"I've lost my hearing aid!" he said in a great panic. He sounded so desperate that I immediately got down on my hands and knees to help look for it. The man reached right past me, and instead of a hand, I saw a harsh metal hook. When he looked up toward me, I realized that the man was blind.

Roland had been an English soldier in Northern Ireland, the land of letter bombs. Every morning, it was his duty to open the general's mail and make sure it didn't contain a letter bomb. One morning, he was not so lucky. A bomb went off in his face, blowing away his eyes, his right ear, and his right hand.

I became good friends with Roland, and he invited me home to meet his wife, Janette, and his baby, Joey. Roland knew the feel of Joey's hair, and the smell of his baby-soft skin, but he would never see his son's face.

Roland had a white cane, and he memorized his mile-long walk to class. Every month, on his own, he took the ferryboat back to England for checkups, tapping his way as he went.

Roland said I could read to him in French every week for practice. I selected a book about the Revelation and Christ's return in the skies. Roland was a Jew, and we had some lively discussions as Joey crawled around on the living room carpet, and Janette washed dishes.

CHAPTER 11

The old Belgian town of Mons was interlaced with cobbled streets and tall, redbrick buildings with ornately carved baroque stone ornaments on the facades. As I walked to the main square one day, I almost didn't notice the little plaque on one of the antique buildings. It read ÉGLISE PROTESTANTE. A little congregation of Reformed Protestants gathered here twice a week. The next time the doors opened, I was there.

It didn't matter that I was a newcomer; they each grabbed me gruffly and planted three kisses on my cheeks: right, left, right. Even the men. It was strange to feel the beards and whiskers of these stout, red-faced men who looked as if they had stepped directly out of Van Gogh's painting of the *Potato Eaters*.

The congregation was small, and several families opened their homes to me immediately. Every Sunday, somebody invited me for lunch and to spend the afternoon, so I was never allowed to become lonely.

Just before Easter, the preacher told us that there was going to be a revival on a barge called the Gospel Ark, which would be coming up the lazy river that ran through Mons. The river was heavily trafficked by huge, sluggish barges that carried gravel and other raw materials through the locks, all the way to Holland.

The Gospel Ark was owned by a long-haired, hippie evangelist and his family. They lived on the boat and taught young people how to evangelize. As soon as the barge arrived in town, we took classes, so we would be ready to help in the crusade.

In the meantime, Madeleine wrote from Scotland that she was having trouble finishing her dissertations. I immediately invited her to come and spend a week with me. I promised during the day to regiment her every waking moment and make her finish her writing. At night, I would show her the town, introduce her to my friends, and take her to the Ark.

"Have you been attending church and growing in your faith?" I asked Madeleine, as I hugged her excitedly at the train station.

"Oh, yes. I've been going to your church in Edinburgh, and I love it. They have special Bible studies for students, and I'm learning so much about the Christian life. I feel as clean as a newborn baby embarking on a great and glorious adventure."

"Great! I'm pleased. I'll take you to some wonderful events while you're here, but first we have to make sure you get your work done."

"You have to stay on my case, Helen. I've already missed two deadlines, and if I don't finish soon, the school won't let me graduate!"

We hailed a taxi and quickly arrived at Madame Lemaire's house. I paid the driver, led the way up the stairs, and opened the door to my room. Madeleine stepped inside.

"Wow, Helen!" she said, surprised to find my mantelpiece adorned with dozens of romantic greeting cards.

"Yes," I said, blushing a little, "José sends me cards and letters several times a week. I spend a lot of time writing back. He's planning to come to London this summer to meet my parents."

Madeleine grumbled as I turned off the alarm, dragged her out of bed, and forced her to write. All day long, I made her sit at the table, writing. By five o'clock, she was ready to break out and see the sights.

We headed for the main square, which was dotted with coffee shops, where students of all races and colors sat and talked. There were a lot of black Africans, and even more Arabs, everywhere. Making our way to the french-fry stand, we each bought some hot, fat fries with mayonnaise, wrapped in newspaper.

"This food is so greasy," I said, "but it's delicious in this cold weather!"

"I love to eat with my fingers, anyway," said Madeleine, "so this suits me fine."

We walked up the hill toward the medieval church, surrounded by green lawns, and sat down on a bench to eat the rest of our fries.

"This is really a quaint little town, Helen" said Madeleine. "What a change from the bustle of Mexico City!"

"You're not kidding. I often wonder what José will think when he comes. I try to picture him here, but it seems so unreal. He says he'll be here in just a few months, but I'm worried about what my parents will say when he comes to London to meet them."

"You don't think they'll approve?"

"Of course not, but what am I supposed to do? I'm the one who has to live with the decision, so I feel as if I'm the one to make the choice. They want me to marry a white, Anglo-Saxon, Catholic professional. They're not going to approve of anyone I choose. I already know that. So I just have to brace myself and make the best of it, I guess."

I wished I could be more optimistic. I dreamed of José every day, but when I tried to picture him with me in my world, a strange uneasiness churned in my stomach.

"Let's go visit Georges and his daughter, Nicole," I said, shaking off my worries and getting up from the bench. "They live just down the hill, and they can give us a lift to the Ark tonight."

We sauntered down the hill and soon arrived at a long road of identical, redbrick houses, where the working class lived. The houses were tiny and all in a row, with just a little brick fence separating one from another. Georges was in the miniature front garden, cutting a rose.

"Bonsoir, Hélène," he said, hugging me affectionately. "Is this your friend, Madeleine?" he said, planting the customary three kisses on her cheeks. "Come in, come in. Nicole is just tossing the salad. You have to join us for dinner."

"We just ate a bag of fries," I volunteered, "but I know Nicole's steaks are irresistible. We were hoping you'd take us with you when you go to the Ark."

"Of course!" he said, opening the door and stepping up the two steep steps into a narrow hallway with dark green wallpaper.

"Nicole! We've got company!" he yelled. A slender girl in blue jeans, with waist-length blond hair, came toward us with a fork in her hand.

"You must be Madeleine," she smiled, leaning toward her, cheek first. "Dinner is almost ready. Just need the drinks, Papa."

Georges led us into a large kitchen with a green tile floor. In the middle, behind a screen, was the bathtub. In front of the tub was a wooden table with two plates set for dinner.

"Put a couple more plates on, Nicole, and I'll go out in the backyard for a little parsley from the garden." Georges wore polyester pants and a bright, plaid shirt. Even though fifty and slightly balding, he walked with the energy of a much younger man.

Georges was a foreman on the railroad. As a young married man, all he had been able to afford was a motorcycle. One day, he and his wife were in a traffic accident. She was killed instantly, leaving him to raise his two small children alone. Through his cheerful laughter, I sometimes detected shadows of his pain and loneliness. He had never remarried.

"So you take care of Georges?" said Madeleine, in perfect French.

"Oh, yes. I get up early and pack his lunch. Then I do the housework and take a long bath in the tub behind you. In the evenings, I usually watch television and iron, while he works in his little garden patch behind the house. Here. The steaks are done. Let's sit down and eat, so we won't be late for the service."

The crusade on the ark was unconventional. The music groups sounded like the Beatles, and the preacher looked like a wild man. Every night, simple people from the surrounding area flooded into the boat, and many went forward at every altar call. I was trained to go up front and talk to them. Being with people at such a moment of honesty with themselves and God was a profoundly touching experience. Madeleine was touched too, and we had a lot to talk about in bed every night. I could tell that her faith was really growing and that her whole outlook on life was undergoing a transformation.

After Madeleine and the Gospel Ark left, I spent even more time praying and fasting. Billy Graham was coming to Brussels that summer, and I wanted to be a counselor in his crusade. I decided to read the French Bible from cover to cover, because I didn't want to be caught unprepared.

As I walked around Mons, I saw young people of all races milling around in the cafes, and I had a profound sense of their spiritual emptiness. I wanted so badly to talk to them about Christ, but many of them were Arab and black African men, so I couldn't just walk up to them in the bars.

However, I could talk to them in the university cafeteria. The ushers seated four students per table, so I had daily opportunities to meet new people. Often the conversation allowed me to talk about my faith. Many times I would stay behind to talk in more depth with one or two of them and maybe even pray with them to accept Christ as their personal Savior.

Whenever that happened, I walked home, overwhelmed with emotion. Each person's faith-quest was so different and so interesting. I hoped that as they returned to their respective countries, the good news of how to have a relationship with God would spread through them to their friends and acquaintances in many parts of the world.

Every Friday night, Georges and Nicole would pick me up and take me to Madame Vincent's house. Madame Vincent was a feisty little old lady with snow white hair and a hug that almost cracked one's ribcage. She lived in a two-room thatched cottage on the outskirts of town. Her floors were Dutch tile. She had a copper kettle on her old, stone stove and a cozy fireplace that burned in the winter.

Madame Vincent must have been the world's greatest prayer warrior. She gave us each a pillow to kneel on, and as we leaned on chairs or couches, Madame Vincent brought the very presence of God into our midst.

We prayed for revival. We prayed for people with spiritual needs. We prayed for the sick and the tormented. When loved ones went into the hospital, we prayed for their healing, and they came out well. When families squabbled, we prayed for reconciliation, and they reconciled. When Nicole started seeing an unsuitable suitor, we prayed especially fervently, and she broke up with him. Praying at Madame Vincent's was like living in a little piece of heaven.

After we had been praying for revival for several weeks, I was in the language school perusing a poster announcing a Christian concert. A young woman named Christine invited me to a small prayer group.

"We've been praying for revival for months also," she said. "We're really excited. We feel it's coming soon. We meet around Michel's kitchen table. He came home one afternoon to find his wife dead on the floor from a brain hemorrhage. In his grief, he turned to Christ. Now we gather weekly in his kitchen to pray."

They welcomed me eagerly and listened as I shared with them how several of the students I had spoken to in the cafeteria had become believers.

"Bring them here! We'd love to have them join us," they said unanimously, and so I did.

A few weeks later, as I was praying in my room one day, in my mind's eye, I suddenly saw José standing in a parched field, trying to dig in the dry, crusty earth. He had written to say he was preaching in a different outlying village where the people were very distrustful of outsiders. The dry earth represented the dryness of their lives.

As he was digging away and merrily singing a song, horrible black clouds began to swirl behind him. A stab of fear passed through my heart. What was the storm? Why was José unaware of it? I wrote to him at once. I told him to run indoors and hide from the approaching storm.

By return mail, the meaning of what I had seen began to unfold. José wrote to say that he had been stricken by a horrible rash on his face. His cheeks were swollen, and the doctors could not decide what the problem was. They had told him he was allergic to sunlight, and he had to stay indoors with the blinds down. He was unable to return to his job, or to preach in the little church in the village.

Then, one day, he wrote to cancel his trip.

"My eyes have been affected, and I can't be in the light at all. I've been confined to my room at my parents' apartment for two weeks. They put blackout curtains on the windows. I can't even turn on a lightbulb. I just sit in the dark and pray. The doctors are afraid I'm going blind."

Now I faced a serious dilemma. Did I love José enough to marry him if he became blind? I tried to picture leading him around, the limitations it would put on our lives, and his looks. Could I be proud of him if he were an invalid? Did I owe it to him to take care of him? Was I strong enough to love him through it? If I wasn't, could I be honest with myself? How did God feel about it? I had asked Him to confirm the marriage by allowing José to come to meet my parents. If he didn't come, would that mean that God was against it?

All my plans were turned completely upside down. I no longer knew what to think. I was tormented for José's sake.

I was tormented for my sake, not knowing what the future held for me. I increased my praying and fasting till I almost didn't eat or sleep. Finally, it all caught up with me. I had to stop everything for three weeks, because I was so stressed and exhausted.

Madeleine had been gone for a few months now, but she was eager to accept my invitation to return to Belgium for the Billy Graham crusade that was to be held in Brussels that summer. There was to be a huge Christian youth festival at the same time, and thousands of young people from all over the world would bring sleeping bags and camp on the floors of the enormous convention center. I had trained for weeks to be a counselor at the crusade, and I couldn't wait for it to begin.

As I took the train to Brussels, I looked idly out the window at the rich, green fields, bordered neatly by irrigation ditches carrying water from the many rivers in the area. The fields were dotted with black-and-white cows, chewing contentedly against a backdrop of willow trees. It was usually drizzly and gray in the winter, but the sun was shining.

Christine was going to join Madeleine and me in Brussels. I had visited Christine's home in the eastern coal mining area of Belgium with its stacks and pits, mounds of waste, and rows of gray houses. But this was southern Belgium, identical in topography to that of Holland, and the scenery was pastoral. Occasionally, the train would pass through a small town with three-story, gray stone houses with lace curtains in the windows, a church steeple, and pastry shops on the cobbled main street.

Pale commuters with mousy hair and bland features stood on the platform in beige overcoats, waiting for the train to Brussels. Every day, thousands of them poured into the city by train, tram, or bus, and disappeared into the myriad of office blocks, which housed the new government of Europe. These and young people from all over the world would be coming to the crusade.

I found Madeleine and Christine in the huge gymnasium that had been set aside as the women's dormitory. Hundreds of sleeping bags were lined neatly on the parquet floors, and the three of us found an open space to set ours down.

During the day, we attended Bible studies. In the evening, we gathered in the huge stadium. Night fell after the altar call, so we could see everything clearly.

First, the choir sang as people poured into the stadium. Then, special soloists came to the microphone with some good, old-fashioned gospel songs. Finally, Billy Graham stood up to preach. Every phrase was immediately interpreted into French. The staccato pauses seemed to give his words a greater urgency.

I was amazed at how simple the message was. Billy Graham had no gimmicks, no cute anecdotes, no scholarly quotations. He just barreled out the gospel story as starkly and simply as it appeared in the Bible. When the altar call came, as if at the push of a button, hundreds of people swarmed down the steps and onto the grass below.

As counselors, we were trained to meet them there. We had some simple literature in our hands. We paired up with the people and talked with them. One night I met a housewife; another night I spoke to an Arab drug addict, who wore fluorescent green contact lenses; another night I helped a naive teenage girl. Each had a story to tell. Each was profoundly touched by God, and through them, so was I.

Billy Graham urged us to continue in the work of evangelism after he left Brussels. Madeleine went back to Britain, but I stayed on, and our youth group volunteered to help in a crusade to be held in a small town south of Mons at the French border.

By this time, classes were over, and since I was just months from graduating with a degree as an interpreter and translator, I had a job at the World Customs Co-Operation Council in Brussels. Every morning, I put on my business suit and beige overcoat and walked thirty minutes to the train station. I commuted an hour into Brussels, took a twenty-minute tram ride to the Council, and went up in the elevator to my private office. It had marble floors and was filled with wall-to-wall dictionaries and manuals.

This international organization coded and classified every single product that crossed any border from one country to another for customs purposes. My boss assigned me a stack of technical translations to work on and provided a Dictaphone, still a novelty in the midseventies. An elderly secretary with white hair and elegant suits, typed up my notes and brought them to me on a gold tray every afternoon.

Occasionally, I went down to the booths to do some interpreting. The subject matter was always tedious. One morning, the world delegates argued for hours on how to classify tennis shoes. The manufacturer was no longer using rubber from Malaysia, and so the shoes had to be reclassified. On another occasion, they spent two days negotiating on the classification of black ink, because again, one of the ingredients had been replaced, and it would make a few pennies difference in the tariff.

Who cares? I thought. I was lonely, isolated in a sterile office with a Dictaphone and marble floors. I was bored in the conference room discussing such inconsequential subjects. I couldn't wait for the clock to strike five when I could get to the really exciting part of the day—talking with people who went forward at the crusade! That would prepare me to be a missionary and speed the day when I would be reunited with José.

CHAPTER 12

After completing my assignment at the World Customs Co-Operation Council in Brussels, I went back to Edinburgh for my final year. I found lodgings with a family in a village just outside town and paid for part of my rent by baby-sitting for them.

The McBrides were strict Scottish Presbyterians. Everything closed down on Sundays, so all we could do was go to church. On Sunday afternoons, Mr. McBride would put on religious music, and we would sit in the living room, drink tea with milk and sugar, and listen to records. He wouldn't let the children play or watch television, which made Sunday the longest day of the week for all of us.

Every letter from José was more worrisome than the previous one. One would say he was coming at Christmastime, the next would say he was going blind. I lived in a constant state of torment, worrying about the

Christmas holidays. As much as I wanted him to come get me, as a knight in shining armor, I just couldn't picture him in my world at all.

To begin with, he looked very Indian. Secondly, he barely spoke English. What appeared to be great charisma in Mexico would look like naiveté in the sophistication of Europe. Deep down, I feared that we were just too different.

At the same time, I had promised to marry him, and my mother had taught me never to go back on my word, no matter what. The suspense was unbearable. I felt unqualified to make a decision myself, so I waited for God to make it for me. If José came, it was God's will for me to marry him; if he didn't, it wasn't.

As I sat in class, trying to focus on the interpreting, my mind would wander back into the web of my dilemma. Christmas seemed to loom very close, and I was terrified. I knew that my parents would be categorically opposed to the marriage. The thought of the conflict that would ensue when I presented a non-Catholic suitor to them was more than I could bear. Literally.

I looked up at the professor's moving lips, and gradually, it all became a blur. I didn't understand a word he was saying. I didn't even know which language he was speaking. I looked at my classmates, and nothing they said made any sense either. Lips moved, and people interacted with each other, but to me, it all sounded like gibberish. I waited for the class to end and ran to the gymnasium pool for a swim in the hopes of clearing my head.

The next day was worse. Finally, after three more days, I gave up. All I could see was people talking at me, but I couldn't grasp anything they said. I couldn't understand what was happening to me. Crying, I rushed for the doors after the last class.

I was close friends with a college professor and his wife, Angie. They had befriended me at the very beginning of my university career, and I was often at their house for meals. Angie was a few years older and wiser than I, and since Madeleine's departure that first year, she had become my closest confidante.

I knew Angie wouldn't ridicule me. I called her and told her I was embarrassed and afraid that I was going insane. She advised me to see a doctor. The doctor assured me there was nothing inherently wrong with me. I was simply having a stress reaction to José's upcoming visit to meet my parents.

Why was it taking so long for me to recover, then, I wondered? How could stress knock me out of almost a whole semester of school? Try as I might, I just couldn't listen to language of any kind. It was as if my mind had just passed out in exhaustion.

I slept. I walked the dogs. I picked up the children from school. But adult conversation, and even the radio and television, were too much for me. I didn't tell my parents that I was missing classes. I wondered what would happen to my grades. I had been at the top of my class for years. Now, in my final year of study as an interpreter, I couldn't even speak English!

Then news came of José's flight reservations. He had to pay for the tickets by closing time on December 6, and he would fly to London via Paris in time to spend Christmas with my family.

I panicked. I wrote and told him I had changed my mind, and asked him to cancel his trip. For a few days I put him out of my mind, but then one night I woke up from a deep sleep and felt compelled to write to him again and invite him to come after all.

I wrote the letter prayerfully, and then plastered the envelope with air mail stamps. I crept out of the house and walked to the bus stop in the cold dawn air. I planned to get on the bus and take the envelope to the post office, so it would go out in the early morning mail. But I decided instead to let God decide how this would all turn out, so I put the envelope in the letterbox outside the house and went back to sleep.

At four in the afternoon, just two hours before the ticketing deadline that fateful day in December, a dejected José arrived at his parents' apartment in Mexico City to see if by chance I had written to change my mind. He had recovered enough to go back to work, and his doctor had given him permission to travel abroad.

"No," his mother said, "there hasn't been any mail for you this week."

"I guess I'll just go down to the travel agency then and cancel my reservation. I'm so shattered. I can't understand why Helenita has done this to me after all these months!"

Just as he was about to leave, the doorbell rang.

"Here is a letter from Scotland covered with air mail stamps," said the postman. "It looked important, so I put it at the top of the stack."

José ripped open the letter and shrieked for joy. My letter had reached him just in time to confirm his flight. He was going to London after all!

I went home for Christmas and helped my mother prepare the guest bedroom. I was very nervous. I kept trying to picture José, his wide grin and victorious look, standing on our doorstep, ready to spirit me away with him into a glorious future in the mountains of Latin America.

At last the doorbell rang. With butterflies in my tummy, I ran to open it. There in the cold, dark night, stood a tired, but jubilant traveler in a maroon polyester suit. I noticed his pants were too short and his socks were sticking out. He looked awkward and out of place as he stepped into our well-lit living room.

My parents greeted him in a civil, but reserved tone, and invited him to step into the living room. He knew little English, so he busied himself handing out gifts of crafts made in Mexico. After a strained, but polite dinner, my parents left us alone in the living room for a few minutes, and we embraced.

The next morning, we went to a department store and bought José a couple of corduroy pants and some lambs-wool sweaters. Clothed in his new outfit, he started to look more presentable.

At last, the big night came. We went into the living room after dinner, and José cleared his throat.

"I came from Mexico because I love your daughter, and I want to marry her," he said simply.

There. The bombshell was finally out. He had said the magic words that, for me, were the key to my future. He had asked for my hand in marriage—that was all I needed to accept his proposal.

My parents objected, of course, and José protested. They were concerned about the primitive living conditions. He told them he had a house, and he would remodel it for me. They were concerned that they might never see me again. He promised them he would keep enough money in savings so I could come back if there ever was an emergency. They said that they were categorically opposed. He said he understood, but that we were adults and simply wanted to share our decision with them.

The following morning when I went downstairs, my father was livid.

"You don't care what we think anymore. You've made up your mind to throw your life away, and that's that. You think you're so grown up, but the man that you plan to marry is nothing but trouble. Just wait. Before long, he'll be beating you!"

"How can you say that?" I protested.

"Just you wait. I know the type. He thinks he's in love with you now, but they're all the same."

"Your father's right," said my mother, who had just walked in the door. "Listen to us. We're your parents. We know what's best for you."

"You don't care what I want, or how I feel. It wouldn't matter who I brought home. You don't want me to marry any Protestant, and you're mad because I'm going to live across the Atlantic. You've never been to Mexico. You don't know what it's like. I've lived there. I have friends there. I'm going to be fine."

"Mark my words," my father said, "this man is not for you. I'll bet you anything he'll give you syphilis!" He turned red with fury and stormed out of the room. "That's what they all do! He'll give you syphilis!"

The door slammed, and I could hear him stomping up the stairs.

"Please listen to us," said my mother, trying to stay calm. "If you really have to go with him, go. But don't marry him for a couple of years. Live with him first. Don't do something so irreversible as marrying him. Please. I'll buy you contraceptives. I don't want you to get pregnant."

I was shocked. Catholic mothers were supposed to warn their daughters to remain chaste, urge them to get married. My mother, one of the most conservative of all, was begging me to live in sin.

"I can't believe you're telling me this," I told her.

"Think about it for a minute. You're white. He's Mexican; he's Indian! What kind of life do you think your children will have if you marry him? They'll be outcasts in his country and outcasts in yours. They won't have a chance!"

"Oh, Mother. These are the seventies! People today aren't prejudiced like that anymore. Lots of young people marry someone of a different race. Anyway, there are many fair-skinned people in Mexico who are descended from the Spaniards. They marry dark-skinned Mexicans, and nobody thinks that is strange, so what's the difference?"

"I'm telling you, dear, you think you know everything. You're young. You're in love. Everything seems so easy. But life is tough, and I don't want to see you suffer."

"What you don't want is a brown-skinned son-in-law and coffee-colored babies! I'm sorry. I've made up my mind. I'm going to leave after graduation and marry José. There's nothing you can do to change my mind."

José and I took the train to Edinburgh for a few days. We got off the train at Princes Street and went straight to the jeweler's to buy an engagement ring. It was New Year's Eve, and as the evening progressed, I decided I would get a room with him at his bed-and-breakfast. I called the McBrides and told them I was out for the evening and would not be back until the following day.

"Alone at last," José said, drawing me close and gazing deep into my eyes when we met in his room as planned. "Your parents watched us like hawks every minute." He stroked my hair, slowly. "I've longed to hold you in my arms for months. At last we have a night alone together." We fell on the bed and kissed. José was getting passionate.

"Slow down," I said. "We can't do this yet!"

"It's all right, Helenita. It's not a sin, so long as we don't actually do it," he said, kissing me even harder. I didn't agree with his reasoning and was prepared to kick him in the groin to preserve my virginity. Fortunately, the evening ended quietly and uneventfully, and I crept back to my room for the remainder of the night.

When I returned to the McBride's the following morning, I could tell there was a storm brewing.

"Your father called. He wants you to call home at once," said Mr. McBride.

"Why? Has something happened?"

"Your parents called last night at midnight to wish you a happy New Year. Of course, you weren't here. This morning, a Mrs. Baird from a bed-and-breakfast called, wanting your parents' number. Said she crept down the back alley last night to peep through the curtains into your room, and she saw you and your young man in there half naked!"

I couldn't believe it. The woman had been spying on us! I called my parents right away. They were sure I was pregnant.

"I can't be pregnant," I protested. "We didn't do anything that would get me pregnant! I can't believe you are such meddlers. I'm twenty-three years old! What are you trying to do to me?"

I called Angie and explained the situation to her. I told her I didn't feel I could go back to the McBride's house after what had happened. She invited me to move in with them and baby-sit their children. I gladly accepted.

José returned to Mexico, and I went back to class. Since I had missed most of the fall semester, my professors agreed to make all my spring-semester grades count double. I was under pressure to perform, but my torment was over, and I felt able to think again. José had come to London, and I was going to marry him as soon as I graduated.

It wasn't but a few days after school started that I came home one afternoon and Angie met me at the door, a pale look on her face.

"Your mother was here today," she said.

"My mother? In Edinburgh? What on earth for?"

She had never made the long trip to Scotland to see me. I couldn't imagine what had brought her to Scotland.

"She came to see us secretly," Angie said. "She asked us not to tell you she was here. Apparently, she had gone to see the head of your department to ask him to keep watch and see if you're pregnant. She wanted us to do the same."

"Are you serious?" I asked, flabbergasted. This was worse than my worst nightmare. I had lived away from home since I was eighteen. My mother, who never took a day off work or traveled anywhere this expensive, had taken a train and come all the way up to Scotland to advise my professor and my friends that I might be pregnant!

I was so angry and embarrassed I could hardly see straight.

"I can't believe that my mother is so intrusive and disrespectful of my personal life. She traveled on the overnight sleeper all the way to Edinburgh, then turned around and went home, all in secret?" I said to Angie. "She has sullied my name at school and tried to turn my friends into spies for her! I am furious!"

If ever I had any misgivings about going to live on the other side of the world, they disappeared completely at that moment. Even as my parents clung desperately to the hope that I would change my mind and accept a job offer in Brussels, I started to save up for my one-way ticket to Mexico.

When I wrote to my mother asking her if she would go to her bank vault and retrieve my birth certificate, without which I could not be married, she refused. After much anguish, I discovered I could hire a lawyer and sign some affidavits. I hoped the Mexican government would accept them, and that I would not run into any red tape as I had previously.

Once the affidavits were safely signed and delivered, I started looking for a wedding dress. After the graduation ceremony, I would move back to Latin America and fulfill my lifetime dream of being a missionary. Since my parents would not be attending our wedding, José booked Saturday, August 26, at the church in Mexico City. He and his extended family were waiting for me with open arms, and all my friends at the church would be thrilled to see me again.

In my suitcase, I put my floor-length wedding dress and train, a simple design that I had picked out on Princes Street; an artificial flower arrangement; a wreath for my hair; two summer outfits; a thick, white sweater; my black, woolen business suit; and my suede coat with the raccoon collar. Folded among these were my radio, tape recorder, and a supply of toiletries. I also had an English cookbook and some small wedding gifts my girlfriends had given me.

My mother made her first official visit to Edinburgh to attend my graduation. When we got back home, my parents reluctantly drove me to the train station in central London. I would cross the channel by ship and catch a flight in Brussels for Mexico City.

We didn't talk much. I had my train ticket, so all we had to do was park and find the platform. The Dover train was there, waiting. I put my luggage inside one of the compartments and then climbed back down onto the platform to say goodbye.

We stood there awkwardly till the guard blew his whistle. At last it was time to embrace and say our last goodbyes. In my hand was my one-way ticket to Mexico. None of us knew if I would ever return.

"Be careful," my mother said, lifelessly.

"Write soon!" echoed my father, as if in a trance.

"Goodbye," I said. "Goodbye!"

I watched them out of the window and waved. They waved back. Their angry, defeated figures grew smaller and smaller. They were bracing themselves. Controlling themselves.

Would I ever see them again?

The train whistled and expelled a stack of smoke. We turned a corner and entered a tunnel; then they were gone.

I made my way to the toilet at the end of the carriage. There, against the deafening noise of the train, I wailed as if my very insides were being ripped from the pit of my stomach, all the way to Dover.

CHAPTER 13

It felt strange to be back in Mexico again. José assured me that once we were married, everything would be wonderful. I wasn't sure. I felt out of place in his parents' high-rise apartment. I slept in one bedroom; nine adults and a baby shared the other two. Trying to sleep, despite the noise of competing radios, televisions, and neighborhood quarrels, was very unsettling. I could never relax.

Only our trips to our future home of San Martin soothed my anxieties and rekindled my dreams. There, José had his old stone cottage with thick walls and red tiles on the roof. He made plans to remodel the house to make it comfortable for me.

"We can knock down this wall and demolish this old stone stove," said his young architect-friend, Juanito, one day as we were inspecting the cottage. I had brought about enough money to buy curtains for the windows. José was talking about reducing the cottage to rubble and starting over.

"How much is this going to cost?" I asked, concerned.

"Don't worry, Princess. Juanito knows what he's doing," José assured me. Juanito looked like an awfully young architect. I didn't know what to think, but I decided that this was not my culture, and I had better stay out of the discussion. After all, José and Juanito sounded as if they knew what they were talking about, and if José wanted to demolish the cottage and build a house on the lot, who was I to question it? Or should I?

I made an appointment for a premarital, gynecological checkup at the government hospital. After examining me, the doctor walked out of the room and left the door facing my stirruped feet wide open. Male doctors and orderlies were passing by, and I was mortified. They obviously had no sense of privacy, since I wasn't even provided with a female nurse.

Since Mexico does not recognize a church wedding, everyone has to be married at the courthouse first. My civil wedding was rather uneventful. José's parents and a couple of witnesses arrived by taxi. We waited in a busy hallway, had a five minute ceremony, and signed all the papers.

As soon as it was over, José was ecstatic. His mother served a lovely lunch in their tiny living room, and then José took me out on a rowboat in Chapultepec Park to celebrate.

The church wedding was to be a couple of weeks later. Mexican tradition held that the groom's family would make all the arrangements, so I just ironed my dress and mailed out the invitations. I entertained a faint hope that my parents might still show up, but it seemed most unlikely. They had made their objections to the wedding plain, and despite my prayers and letters to them, there was no evidence that they would change their minds, much less fly halfway around the world to bless this union.

Fortunately for me, in place of my father, Howard Klassen from the Wycliffe Institute agreed to give me away. Karen, one of the translators, would be my maid of honor. The girls at the church were all hoping to be my brides-maids, but I felt that since I had crossed the Atlantic alone, and since none of my friends or family would be present, I would rather stand at the altar alone too.

Before the wedding, I stayed with Howard and his wife at the Institute. Howard was in a great mood. He borrowed a beige limousine from a friend and rented a tuxedo for himself. Karen offered to dress me. She joked and laughed as she worked. My nervousness mounted as she added the flowers and veil.

According to Mexican custom, we were to go first to the studio to have our portrait taken. My visions of not being seen by the groom until I came down the aisle were shattered. Things were already very different from what I was used to, so I abandoned all thoughts of control and graciously accepted their plans.

Howard helped me into the limousine, and we drove to the photographer's. As the car stopped at the curb, José stepped forward to open the door for me.

"Wow, Princesita! You look gorgeous!" he said, smiling in delight. He was dressed in his new, navy suit, white shirt, and pale blue silk tie. His jet black hair was shining, his white teeth were gleaming, and his eyes were radiant. He was jubilant.

"You are the most beautiful woman in the universe. Did you know you are my greatest achievement and my most coveted prize? In Mexico, we think fair-skinned women are so much more lovely than the dark-skinned ones. You are not only fair, but educated, sophisticated, beautiful, classy. Everyone is impressed that you are marrying me. I'm the luckiest man on earth to have won you for myself, and I will always be proud to have you at my side."

The photographer sat me in a chair and arranged my bouquet of white flowers gently in my hand. José stood proudly by my side, and we smiled as the photographer immortalized the moment.

Then I got back into the limousine with Howard, and we drove to the church. There were crowds of people outside, all waiting to see the bride arrive. I felt almost like royalty! As the limousine stopped in front of the door, the ushers pushed the people aside to help me in. We climbed to the top of the stairs and stood behind the red velvet drapes separating the lobby from the sanctuary. The people were quickly seated, and we waited for the organ to begin.

As the first chords of "Here Comes the Bride" resounded, Howard squeezed my hand, and we stepped forward. The drapes were drawn aside, and we made our way slowly down the long, carpeted aisle. The cameras flashed, and the crowds smiled at us from either side. At the front stood the well-dressed groom, glowing with pride.

A full orchestra playing popular love songs was in the choir loft. Having come from Presbyterian Scotland, I was expecting Bach and other solemn organ recitals. I was crushed. After all, this was my wedding, and where I came from, the bride helps select the music; but they had gone to such expense to get the orchestra, how could I complain?

As the preacher rose for the sermon, a tremendous afternoon thunderstorm broke. Even as his voice reverberated in the microphone, the raindrops ran down the window panes, and the flashes of lightning were followed rapidly by crashing booms of thunder. It was almost Wagnerian.

We stood for the vows and were pronounced man and wife. José raised my veil and kissed me, and we walked back down the aisle as Señor and Señora Mendez.

There were over five hundred people at the formal reception, including little old ladies in the church who had responded to our open invitation. We stood in the receiving line as one by one they hugged and kissed us.

"So where are you going for your honeymoon?" several people asked.

"It's a surprise," José told them.

They seated us at the head table, and the women of the church served all the guests a hot meal. I was worried about the expense to José's family, but they seemed to be intent on making this a great day for us, so I decided to have a good time.

"Give me your shoe," said one of the men, looking at me with a twinkle in his eye.

"My shoe?" I asked. "What on earth for?"

"You'll see," he said.

Fortunately, I had bought brand new shoes for the wedding, so I wasn't embarrassed to hand one to him.

"Oh, no!" he exclaimed. "It's a sling-back! You won't go far on your honeymoon with this shoe."

In a little while, the shoe arrived back at my table stuffed with money.

"The guests all pitched in so you would have a nice honeymoon!" cooed the old ladies around us. "Now the next custom is for you to get up on a chair, and throw your bouquet back over your head!" I hated all these customs, but that's what the people expected, so I climbed up on a chair and threw the bouquet. Then I slipped into comfortable clothes, and Howard drove us to our downtown hotel, where we had a room reserved for our wedding night.

"Tonight is very special," said José. "This is our wedding night. Everything is going to be exquisite. This will be a night of love you will never forget. According to the Bible, there is supposed to be blood on the wedding sheets as a sign of the marriage covenant, and you never know, we might even make a baby!"

"Don't be too disappointed if there is no blood, José. Remember, I told you that I have been using tampons and riding horses for years. I've read in doctors' pamphlets that sometimes women who have done that don't bleed."

"Come here and stop worrying," he said, beginning to unbutton my silk blouse. I was drained from the emotions of the wedding and fell on the bed, exhausted. What followed fell way short of my expectations. As far as I was concerned, it was just a memorably painful evening, and there was no blood on the sheets.

The next morning, José was quiet.

"Is something wrong?" I asked.

"According to the Old Testament, a woman who doesn't bleed on her wedding night can be returned to her father because she is not a virgin. I've been struggling with the idea for a while, but I don't think I'll do it," he said magnanimously. "It would be too embarrassing."

"I told you before we were ever engaged that I had been using tampons all these years."

"I know you did. But how am I supposed to believe you are a virgin?"

"Because I told you I was. Don't you believe me? There's nothing I can do to prove it to you except to tell the truth."

"Are you telling the truth?"

"Of course I am!"

There was nothing more I could add to the subject, so I put it out of my mind. Years later, I would find out that he never really believed me.

"So where are we going for our honeymoon?" I asked him.

"You remember my friend Luis, who came up for the wedding from Veracruz? He said he's driving back down to the coast today, and he'll take us with him."

Driving in the back of a Volkswagen bug with Luis wasn't exactly my idea of a romantic getaway. Especially when I realized that the road to Veracruz was narrow and winding, descending steeply for several thousand feet, and that Luis was a Mexican cab driver. He lunged forward and overtook every truck in our way, chatting merrily with José as he did so. Halfway to the coast it started to pour, and then night fell, obscuring our vision completely.

We spent our honeymoon on the lush Caribbean coast in a clean, modern hotel on the beach. Luis told José he could borrow his cab for a couple of days. José assured me he knew how to drive, but he banged the car into the wall twice, just getting it out of the hotel parking garage. I was mortified for Luis' sake, but José just laughed it off.

I should have realized that the honeymoon was just a foretaste of what lay ahead.

CHAPTER 14

After the honeymoon, we moved into the only livable room of José's cottage in San Martín. We painted it white, using limestone. I had brought a few wall decorations with me, and José's mother bought us a bright orange bedspread and sheets. Other wedding guests had donated pots, pans, an iron, and some silverware.

There was no refrigerator in the room, so every morning I would walk up the cobbled hill to the marketplace and fill my bag with oranges, potatoes, tortillas, and beef. As I made my way down the hill, the bags were heavy, but the sun was shining, and my heart was happy. José was at school until almost three, so I had all morning to myself.

The local workmen knocked down the rest of the house. They started to build twelve-foot walls around the property and construct the shell of the new house. It wasn't long before the money ran out, and as with so many other Mexicans, we planned to finish the house—someday.

Since I was a foreigner, I was not allowed to be employed in Mexico. My only job was to learn to fit into the culture and be accepted by the people. Living the rustic life was quite a vacation for me, and I enjoyed doing my chores and listening to the Christian programs that were being transmitted via shortwave radio in various languages from Quito, Ecuador.

Once a week, I would take the laundry outside into the sunshine. There was a concrete washboard and sink out in the patio. It was much too low for me because I was so tall, but I didn't mind bending over and scrubbing our sheets and clothes by hand. There was no hot water, but if I waited until noon or so, the sun would take the chill out of the pipes, and the water wasn't too cold. The patio was crisscrossed with clothes lines, so I would hang the washing out to dry and then plan to spend the following morning ironing.

On the table in our little room, I had a two-plate electric burner. I made first one dish, and then another on it. Once José arrived, he wanted to eat immediately. I couldn't bear the idea of standing at the stove and heating his tortillas while he ate as his mother and sisters did, so I persuaded him to let me put the hot plates directly onto the table, so we could eat together and watch the tortillas on the burner.

After lunch, we would go for long walks in the countryside or visit friends. José's grandparents were our favorites in the village. In the evenings, we stayed home. We had no television, so we listened to his small record collection, or played Chinese checkers at the house of his boss, the school principal.

Every Friday, we took off for Mexico City as soon as school was out. José insisted on seeing his family at least weekly, so there was hardly a weekend when we weren't in the city. Usually, we all stayed up late on Saturday night, laughing around the dining room table until late into the night. José's family accepted me totally, now that we were married. His mother made it her personal mission to make me feel completely comfortable, cooking special dishes for me to make me feel good.

Every Sunday morning, while it was still dark, we took a cab to the bus station and went out to the tiny village, way up in the mountains, where José was pastor. Our bus dropped us at an intersection with a mud road that led to the village. From there, a rickety local bus took us to the church, along muddy roads lined with cornfields.

The church was built simply: concrete blocks covered in limestone. The benches were of plain wood. As in almost every rural Protestant church in Mexico, a loud electric band that played out of tune and out of tempo, was situated next to the altar. The band members would close their eyes, singing loudly and off-key, while the congregation joined in, clapping their hands and swaying to the sound of the music.

The men sat on one side, taking off their dusty cowboy hats as a sign of respect. Their clothes were torn, their hair disheveled, their teeth yellow, and their fingernails black. The women sat on the other side, their long braids trailing down the backs of their colorful clothing. Many of them carried a baby in a reboso shawl or held on to toddlers with uncombed hair and scruffy clothes. Despite the bitter cold, most of them wore plastic sandals over bare feet.

These particular Masahua Indians were very wary of outsiders. My role was simply to smile and let José do most of the talking. He had been preaching to them for almost two years, and he was just beginning to gain their confidence.

After the service, we always would go to one of their homes for a surprise lunch. They loved to feed us and tell us their life stories. One particular Sunday, José chose to visit Maria. She was the single mother of Conchita, a little red-faced five year old. Maria said she would run ahead to prepare the lunch.

"My house is the last one way up there near the top of the mountain," she said, pointing across the barren brown earth to the dark blue mountaintop. "It's about an hour's walk."

Halfway there was a wide river, swollen with the autumn rains. We got into a tiny boat. The boatman pulled us across by hand, holding onto a thick cable that crossed the river.

Maria was thrilled to see us coming. All she had left in her kitchen were two potatoes, three eggs, one tomato and some tortillas. She was busy heating the tortillas and frying an omelet when we arrived. In the hut was a large bed where Maria and Conchita slept, a table and two chairs, and a stone stove.

"It's pretty desolate here, Maria." José said.

She smiled. "I don't mind. It's hard in the wintertime because it's so far to walk. Sometimes it's too dangerous to cross the river. But we're happy here."

The flames were dancing on her stone stove, casting a red hue over the simple room in the early evening dusk. We crept closer to enjoy its warmth as we listened to Maria's banter.

"Conchita is really smart, you know. She loves to go to church. Sometimes when I get mad at her, she recites something she heard in church, and it makes me ashamed!"

"How come you're alone here?" asked José.

"Oh, I had one of those typical husbands. He'd get drunk, and he'd beat me. I cried a lot. Then he just left. We haven't seen him since Conchita was a baby. Here, let me give you another tortilla." She was so thrilled that we had come to visit. Even though she was poor, she gave us all the remaining food in the house.

We spent a wonderful evening talking and sharing together. By the time we crossed the river and walked back to the village, it was pitch black and freezing cold. The last bus had already left for the main road.

"Let's knock on the door of the Perez family. They may have an extra bed," suggested José. For him, everything was an adventure.

The Perez family was almost ready to turn out the single bulb burning above the kitchen table and go to bed. As in all Mazahua huts, there was no heating, and the temperature was well below freezing.

They cleared off a bed that had been occupied by a sleeping baby. It turned out to be flea-infested and wet with urine, but it was a bed, and we slept on it. Early the next morning, before the cock had even crowed, we were on the first bus back to San Martín. José could not be late for school.

One evening, José and I were standing in one of the unfinished rooms of our house, talking. It was dark, and there were no window panes in the windows as yet. As we talked, a truck made its way noisily down the hill, right in front of the house.

As the truck passed, I automatically looked up at its headlights. José let the truck go by, and then, completely without warning, he slapped me across the face. My cheek burned red as fire. I was stunned.

"Why did you look at the man in the truck?" José lashed out at me.

"I didn't. It was a reflex action. I saw lights, and I looked up at the truck. I didn't see the driver until he was almost in front of the window!"

Never in my wildest dreams had I imagined that José would hit me. I wanted to break down and cry, but I was too proud. Years of training on the British stiff upper lip made me hold my wild and confused emotions in check until I could sit down and think clearly about what had happened. Uncontrolled passions were scorned in Britain. I had to calm down and use my brain to figure out what to do.

When José went to work the next morning, I began to think rationally about my options. I could walk out on him and go . . . where? I had no money to go anywhere. I was too embarrassed and too humiliated to go back to my parents. I couldn't get a job in Mexico City because I was a foreigner. So where else would I go? I had made my choice and married the man of my dreams, so now all that was left to do was to stick it out.

Yet my father's warning rang in my ears. He had predicted that José would beat me. What would he think if he were to walk down the hill to my muddy street and find me living in my single concrete room without a toilet or a shower for my basic necessities? What would he say if he saw his daughter, an international interpreter, in a poor Mexican village with a man who slapped her because she looked up at a passing car?

I was so ashamed, I didn't know what to do. I was living on the other side of the world, far from people who knew me. I was trying to fit into an alien culture and not disappoint my husband. I was working on winning the confidence of the local people. I had made no close friends, and

José had forbidden me to share any personal or marital problems with anyone outside the family.

I had nobody to talk to, and I was too proud to run. As José's mother would always say to him, "You've made your bed; now lie in it!"

So I put on a nice smile and went to the door to kiss José when he arrived home from work as if nothing in the world had ever gone wrong. I was masquerading as the contented little wife and stuffing my hurt and anger deep into my soul.

CHAPTER 15

Days turned into weeks, and weeks into months. The snow was falling in the mountains surrounding us. The water in the faucet was ice-cold now, and I lay very still under the blankets until the sun was high in the sky every day. The little concrete room was cold. Even the little electric heater José bought for me wasn't enough to keep me warm.

We spent Christmas in Mexico City with José's family. They agreed with José that it was time to resign from the village church and focus his evangelism on starting a church in San Martín, where we lived.

Shortly after we returned to our little house in San Martín, we ran into a man named Paco. Paco had been a poor man, driving trucks from Tijuana to Guatemala to make a living. Little by little, he had acquired an estate: first a wife, then children, and then a chicken farm. He rented some empty rooms in San Martín and started to raise chickens.

They lived within walking distance of our house and offered to hold the services in the chicken coop. Soon we were the best of friends. When his wife, Ernestina, went into the hospital to have her fourth baby, José and I went up the hill to their house every day. I shopped and cooked and took care of the children. José provided moral support.

Once a month, Paco drove his truck over the mountains to Mexico City to buy baby chicks. In the palm of his hand he carried the money he needed to bribe the officials along the highway. The police always blocked the road at a certain curve, and you had to have your money ready, or you weren't allowed through. And if you gave them too little, they would act insulted and demand more.

Once in the capital, Paco would go to the main produce market to buy dozens of crates of tiny, furry little chickens to take home. His children helped feed them. When they were big enough to run around the farmyard, Paco would drive from village to village, selling two here, and three there, for people to fatten up and then eat.

Paco was excited about God and began to give generously to the growing little church. He worked long, hard hours, and his business thrived. His wife and children helped, and his savings account grew. He hired some laborers and bought more chickens. One day, at the prayer meeting, he was really in a good mood.

"I bought a couple of acres down by the main road," he said proudly. "God willing, I'll build a house and five chicken barns."

"See how God blesses you when you put Him first and tithe," said José. "You can never outgive God!"

Paco built a tall brick wall to surround his new property, and felt sure that now his little kingdom was safe. Paco only had one problem: his sons were not bright. Night after night, he would plead with them.

"Do your homework, sons, so you won't have to labor as hard as I have. Cold, rain—without an education you have to brave it all!"

His eldest son, twelve year old Miguelito, always cringed at his father's words. He chewed on his pencil and stared out the window, longing to get on his bicycle and ride around the farmyard among the dogs and chickens. Maybe one day he would inherit the farm and not have to worry about a formal education.

It was Miguelito's job to turn up the gas heaters for the chickens before he went to bed every night. The hired hands slept on the hay in one of the chicken houses, so they could keep an ear out for the barking dogs.

One night, as dawn was about to break, Paco tossed in his sleep. Somewhere in his subconscious, he knew something was wrong. As his body tossed, his mind struggled to awaken. He was right. He could smell something. Smoke! Fire!

Panic propelled him to his feet. He ran like a madman to the door. Instantly he realized that the chicken houses were on fire. He rushed wildly from one coop to another. Chickens were cackling everywhere. But where were the hired hands? Why weren't they helping?

"Pepito! Santiago! Mochis! Get out here! Help! Quick!" Paco shouted, frantically.

Ernestina, his wife, came running, followed by the startled children.

"Lazy helpers! What is it with you?" Paco yelled.

Rushing to the helper's barn, he immediately saw what the problem was. Thick fumes were everywhere. Amid the smoke, he could distinguish his three helpers lying limply asleep in the hay.

"Ernestina, boys! Hurry!" he screamed, shaking first one helper, then the other.

They were not asleep; they were unconscious—maybe even dead!

"Oh, God, help me get them out of here alive," Paco prayed.

Ernestina and the children coughed and spluttered in the smoke. They struggled with the heavy bodies, pulling and heaving, till all three men lay on the moist earth outside.

"Quick, Miguelito! Jump on your bicycle and go to town for some help," said Paco, trying to fan the smoke victims back to life. He grabbed the hose and started to spray water over the leaping flames. Hundreds of burnt chickens lay smoldering in the ashes. His farm was gone, his helpers half dead, his business destroyed.

There was, of course, no insurance. There was only the prospect of years of hard work to get back on his feet again.

Miguelito pedaled as fast as he could into town to wake the night watchman at the town hospital. The old man woke with a jolt and ran to summon the paramedics who drove the old ambulance.

After he had summoned help, Miguelito was overcome with guilt. He had forgotten to turn up the gas tanks. A failure at school, he had now failed in his role as eldest son and heir to the chicken farm. His only option now was to run away from home in disgrace!

We found Paco weeping in his kitchen the next day. His son had been missing for over twelve hours, his farm was smoldering in ashes, and his wife was inconsolable.

"What worth is my farm and all I have, if I have lost my eldest son?" he cried.

We did our best to comfort him. We had prayer meetings and special services, but nobody saw or heard from Miguelito.

Finally, about two weeks later, tired of being a vagabond, Miguelito turned himself in at the city hall, and his parents were called to pick him up. José and I were walking home from the market when Paco's truck passed by in the distance. Ernestina was sitting in the back holding her son, tears streaming down her face.

The school year progressed slowly, and by late spring, the sun came up a little sooner, allowing me to go outside again. Since we had no bathroom, I would boil a saucepan of water on my hot plate, then mix it with a bucket of cold water. Then I would stand in the far corner of the walled courtyard, strip naked, and pour the water over myself with a jug. The walls were high, and there were no tall buildings around us, so nobody could see me.

Occasionally, José would take me to his school where he was now vice principal. He showed me the leather belt he used to discipline his twelve-year-old students.

"Some of these children are as stubborn as mules," he said. "If they won't listen to reason, I have to whip them. The others see it, and they settle down in a hurry."

"Doesn't it hurt?" I asked.

"Of course it does! It's supposed to."

"They whipped boys at the boys' school in London, but I never heard of a girl getting the belt."

"Usually the girls behave better," he said. "But not always. Someone has to show them who's boss!"

He invited me to the folk-dance festivals and ceremonies held in the school yard on political holidays. Each village had its patriotic celebrations, and the village school was the center of local color on such occasions. They seemed to venerate their revolutionary heroes as if they were gods.

After the ceremony, the children would go back to class, and I would spend the rest of the day with one of two women friends in the village. The first, a poor woman who had chapped hands from standing at the sink all day, loved to have me listen to her troubles. The second, a rich woman, was flattered by my company, feeling it raised her social status in the village. I always dressed nicely wherever I went, so as not to insult the people.

Once in a while, José would take me on a bus trip to other parts of Mexico. Sometimes we went with his whole family. One night, all of us were returning from seeing the mummies in the museum in Guanajuato, when we missed our connection. It was four o'clock in the morning, and José's brother had misplaced the tickets, so they wouldn't let us on the connecting bus.

We fussed at him because it was so cold, and we had to wait a long time for the next bus. When we reached Mexico City, we heard that the bus that we had missed had been in a wreck. Eleven people had been killed and eighteen had been seriously injured. We bought the gory scandal sheet, popular in Mexico, and sure enough, graphic pictures of the injured and dead were splattered across the front page.

Of course we were stunned at God's preserving grace and eagerly went to church in Paco's kitchen the following Sunday to give Him thanks for our miraculously safe arrival in the capital.

CHAPTER 16

"I don't know why it is," I told José some time in mid-March, "but I can't even hold Ernestina's newborn on my lap when I'm sitting down. I feel so weak." We had government health insurance, so I asked him if he would take me to get a checkup at the clinic in the industrial town of Toluca. José kept putting it off, and I didn't think it was a good idea for me to travel there unaccompanied.

Yet, despite his reluctance to take me to a doctor, he did not hesitate to force me on the bus to see his mother every Friday night.

"Can't we just take one weekend off and stay here in the village? I am so exhausted. I don't feel well. The weekly bus trip is so tiring. Plus, I think we should consider ourselves a family. I think you are too addicted to your mother. You know the Bible says that a man should leave his parents and cleave to his wife."

"You leave my mother out of this. She's my mother, and I love her. Besides, I miss her wonderful cooking. I do plenty of cleaving to you during the week. It is scriptural to honor one's parents, even after one is married. You don't have a loving family as I do, so you don't understand how much I need them. A week without seeing them is all I can stand. So the discussion is closed. We'll continue going home on weekends."

I was disappointed and exasperated but too tired to fight. A few days later, José came home from school in a bad mood. He put his record player on as loud as he could and played his favorite record of military marches over and over again. By dinner time, the record was getting on my nerves, and I asked him if he would take it off. He just turned it up louder. At a quarter of nine, I told him I couldn't stand it any longer. He yelled at me, turned his back and went to sleep, the music still blaring.

The next morning, I waited until he was gone, and I took the bus to Toluca to see the doctor. He ran some tests and told me to return in a week. After the appointment, I walked down the busy boulevard, looking in the shop windows. José had government health and retirement, but he didn't make very much money. What he made, we spent on food and cheap public transportation.

I was hoping to catch a glimpse of a white steel cabinet that I had seen in a few women's houses. I passed a furniture store and saw they had one. I looked at the price tag. It would take years of saving; I didn't think we would ever be able to afford it. For the first time, it began to dawn on me just how poor we really were.

From there, it was only a short walk to visit José's uncle, Reverend Fidencio, and his family, who had recently moved from their hovel in San Martín to an unfurnished apartment in Toluca.

Preachers in Mexico were supposed to live below the poverty line and eat beans and rice. Reverend Fidencio and his wife, Elvira, were struggling in the ministry to pay their medical bills and keep their seven children alive and studying.

"What brings you here, Helenita?" asked Aunt Elvira, smiling as she led me straight to the kitchen table to share in the afternoon snack. Hot chocolate and sweet breads was all the family could afford for dinner every night, so I helped myself and told them about my doctor's appointment.

We talked for a long time about this and that. The longer I stayed, the more comfortable I became, and the more I started to realize how miserable I was with José. Finally, I began to cry.

"What's going on, Helenita?" asked Uncle Fidencio, in a kind, concerned manner.

"You can tell us," pleaded Aunt Elvira. "We know married life isn't always easy. Is José not treating you right?"

Her gaze was so inviting, but I was terrified to answer her question. I was afraid of breaking confidence and tattling on José. He had always told me that family problems should never be discussed outside the home.

"Has he been hitting you?" asked Uncle Fidencio.

I looked down.

"I knew it!" said Aunt Elvira. "I've felt for a while that things weren't going quite right. Have you talked to your in-laws?"

"No," I said, "I wouldn't dream of it."

"Well, you should," said Aunt Elvira. "José was a real discipline problem when he was growing up, but his parents were able to handle him. You should talk to them. They'll straighten him out for you."

Just then there was a knock on the door. I wiped my eyes. José had read the note I had left him and had followed me to Toluca. It was dark and time to go back home. I hugged Aunt Elvira and felt relieved that at last, I had been able to talk to someone.

The lab tests showed that I had histolytic amoebas, allegedly the toughest type of amoebas to kill. I was so weak, I could barely walk from the house to the bus stop. I started immediately on the treatment.

The next time I was alone with José's mother, I confided in her. She and his father pulled José into their bedroom and reasoned with him behind closed doors until deep into the night. For a few weeks, things improved, but it wasn't long before he was back to his old self again.

When I returned for testing to see if the treatments had killed the amoeba, the doctor had disappointing news.

"We'll have to try again, Señora Helenita. This medicine did not work. I'll prescribe something stronger. Follow my instructions carefully, and return again in May."

I was very weak and had lost a lot of weight. I tried to get José to slow down so we wouldn't be on the go so much. I couldn't keep walking up the hill for the heavy groceries every day and then rushing frantically to Mexico City every Friday, but José refused to stay in San Martin. He said he had to see his family. As a concession, he let me go to church with them in Mexico City and then take the noon bus back to San Martín on Monday.

Finally, just before school ended, the doctor told me the treatment had succeeded, and the amoebas were gone! José dropped me off in Mexico City to spend a week at the

Wycliffe Translators' Institute with Howard and his wife, while he graded his students' final exams.

That night I started to vomit, and by midmorning, Howard had taken me to the hospital. The doctor looked into my yellow eyes and immediately diagnosed hepatitis. He ordered complete isolation and a special diet. I was to chew candy all day long. He said it would help my liver, since it could digest sweets, but not fats.

Howard arranged for me to move into an empty room at the institute. It had a small bathroom and a kitchenette. The Wycliffe nurse, Celia, who happened to be from England, brought food to me on a tray from the dining room. Nobody else could come in.

The room was dark and seemed to keep spinning around, and I kept throwing up. Celia brought wet towels to hold on my forehead and checked on me several times a day, bringing food and medication. The week blended into one long night.

When José returned to Mexico City the following weekend, Howard gave him the bad news. José rushed out to the local supermarket to buy me bags of candy to cheer me up. The doctor said that José could move in with me, provided he took a gamma globulin injection, as did Celia, her family, and everyone in the institute.

José was embarrassed at the expense I had caused Howard, since everyone at the institute had to have shots because of me. Why did I have to fall sick there? He was frustrated. Day after day, he brought my meals from the dining room. Then he sat beside my bed and cut the food up into little pieces, so I could pick it up with my fork.

In the mornings, he would brush my teeth, as I didn't have enough strength to lift my toothbrush and seesaw back and forth. Every other day he would shampoo my hair, as I was too weak to raise my hands to my head.

José pushed my bed to the window so I could see out. Nobody else could visit me; they could only look at me through the window. Occasionally, someone would stop by my window and wave at me. I felt like a zoo exhibit. Some called me on the phone, but I was too weak to hold the receiver and talk for long. Books became my closest companions. For hours I lay without moving. Whenever I didn't sleep, I read.

Most of the time, I lay limply in my bed. I cried a lot. I cried for good reason and for no reason. When José left every morning for summer school, I cried because I was lonely. When he went to church on Sundays, I cried because I couldn't go. I cried because my parents hadn't written for a year. I cried because I wasn't getting any better. I cried during the day, and I cried at night.

May turned into June, June into July. Soon it would be August. The books said hepatitis lasts about a month; but I had been so weak from the amoebas when I contracted the hepatitis, and I had previously had malaria, which is also a liver disease, so I was taking a long time to recover.

Every week I had to go to the hospital for a checkup. José would go on ahead at about 4:00 A.M. It was cold and dark. He stood in line until the hospital opened at seven, and then he was given an appointment number. He would rush back to the institute and wait on the curb till a taxi passed. Then he would run in, pick me up, and carry me to the cab. I would lie on the backseat. Each bump in the road used up some of my energy.

I would sit on the plastic chairs, sometimes for an hour, sometimes two or three, until my number was called. Often, the chair was too uncomfortable for me, and I was too weak to sit, so I would lie on the stone floor in the hallway.

After a while, José got tired of chasing taxis. He took our tithe, and with the help of his father, he bought a beaten up old Volkswagen. But the Volkswagen turned out to be a stolen vehicle, and he went through much grief and money trying to make it legal.

Day after day, I chewed candy. At night I would count the number of wrapping papers on my bedside table: 85, 79, 103. The pounds crept on, but health was still nowhere in sight.

One day José broke down. His patience snapped, and he yelled a lot. He walked out and slammed the door behind him. I cried all day. In the evening, he knelt by my bed and said he was sorry.

"When I married you, I thought you were as perfect as a beautiful porcelain doll. It never occurred to me that you were human and could break. I had you up on a pedestal, and when you fell ill, I just could not accept it. My family and friends keep asking how you're doing, and all I can say is, 'She's still sick!'"

In August I began to play the minute game. I had been in isolation for over two months, and I had built up enough strength to be out of bed for about ten minutes a day. But when you add up how long it takes a sick person to shuffle to the bathroom and back a few times a day, ten minutes are quickly gone.

Day after day I kept time, trying to break the ten-minute record. One day I made it to twelve minutes, but the next day I was too sick to even make nine. Every day Celia came to check on me, bringing her injection tray with her. Every day she cheerfully inquired how I was doing and expressed sympathy with my lack of progress.

Would I ever get well? Hope seemed so elusive. I had set some goals; I wanted to increase my time out of bed by two minutes each day, but I just couldn't make it. Three weeks went by. Nineteen minutes; then back to twelve again. Would I ever recover from this disease, or would I remain its victim forever? Even crying exhausted me needlessly.

José was aggravated that I was taking so long to get well. One morning he insisted that I get up early and make him some scrambled eggs. In my weakness, I reached for the bottle of oil and started to mix the eggs. They seemed to be unusually stringy. When I tasted them to see what the problem was, I realized that instead of oil, I had used Pine-Sol floor disinfectant!

In September the doctor said I wasn't getting better.

"I'll give you forty-eight hours to leave the smog and the high altitude of Mexico City," he said. "If you stay in this place, you will develop cancer on top of all this!"

José applied for a transfer to a lower altitude. I couldn't go to the jungle because of my history of malaria. All that was left was the desert, and that is where he was assigned.

On September 15, 1977, just one year after our wedding, José carried me onto a plane, which took us to the desert of the Baja Peninsula. It would be two years before I would be well again.

CHAPTER 17

Getting off the plane in La Paz, the capital of the Baja
Peninsula, was like opening the door to a blast furnace. Since most of the city had only ceiling fans, life during the summertime slowed down to a snail's pace. The
people lay on their hammocks or sat inertly in their door-
ways, waiting for the heat to pass.

An unshaven old taxi driver in white pants and a som-
brero complied with José's request of driving us to something "good, pretty, and cheap." The yellow hotel was built
of concrete with tall ceilings. There was no air conditioning, so I lay on the bedsheets for hours, watching the ceiling fan rock and wobble in our upstairs room. The large
windows were wide open, and occasionally, I would sit on
the windowsill and look down at the street outside.

La Paz, the capital of the province, was an international
port. Cruise ships occasionally would dock, spilling their

eager passengers onto the shores to hunt for treasures among the duty-free shops. However, it was September, and very few tourists were visible in the streets below. The shops closed for the noon siesta, and only the moaning of the radio at the barber's shop could be heard in the heat of the day.

José spent his time at the government offices, processing his transfer. I stayed in the room. Three times a day I would shuffle downstairs to the ceramic tile restaurant where old Javier served ranch-style eggs with beans and chile for breakfast, fried fish with guacamole and rice for lunch, and thin steak and french fries for dinner.

One evening before sunset, José took me for a slow walk down the street to look in the shop windows. The low buildings were painted in pastel colors and the windows were full of merchandise from all over the world. It had been a long time since I had seen anything other than Mexican goods, and I was delighted.

We walked to the end of the main street, and there the road ended. The remainder of the city had streets of sand, and the people lived in fragile little houses with electrical wires hooked clandestinely into occasional electrical poles.

"You should consider yourselves lucky that you weren't here when the dam burst," said old Javier, as he served us dinner that night. "That's when I lost my wife and kids. Only the scruffy dog survived."

"What happened?" asked José.

"There was a hurricane and the dam burst, killing most of the people in the neighborhood."

"How could that happen?" I asked.

"Oh, it's typical of the government. The Ministry of Works sent a lot of money here from Mexico City for the construction of that dam. All the engineers involved in the project helped themselves to part of the money, so there was only enough left for substandard construction. Then they bribed the inspectors, and the permit was granted. When the disaster happened, President Echeverría flew over to see the damage. He shouldn't have bothered. We threw tomatoes at him."

When José's transfer papers were completed, we took a taxi to the bus station and bought tickets for our twelve-hour trip through the desert in a bus without air-conditioning. The bus left the station, rolling slowly down the sandy streets, past the ramshackle hovels of cardboard and corrugated roofing that the people lived in.

Once on the tarmac highway, it picked up speed. There was only one lane going in each direction, but the traffic was light. For the first hour, we drove through plain sandy desert. Only the occasional shack, rusty old car, or circling buzzard would break the monotony of the view.

After a while, the scenery became more interesting as the road started to rise onto the rocky hills that followed the coastline. For the rest of the day, three colors burned themselves into my vision: the shimmering white of the rocks, the prickly green of the cacti, and the glistening blue of the sea.

We stopped for lunch at a cheap, roadside cafe that served Cokes, fried fish, rice, and a newspaper to kill the flies with. After a trip to the smelly outhouse that served as the ladies room, we climbed back onto the bus and into the sticky plastic seats to continue our journey.

By nightfall, we reached Santa Rosalía, a forsaken village of colorful shacks and red earth roads. Howard had given us the names of some missionaries, and they were glad to give us a bed for the night.

The following morning, Glen, the elderly missionary, volunteered to drive us to El Vizcaíno, the village where José was going to teach.

"It's about a two-hour drive, but I'd be glad to take you and help you find a place to stay." We climbed into his rusty, old pickup truck and rolled down the windows.

Glen took the highway inland. As far as the eye could see, there were cacti trees, white rocks, and sand. In the background were blue silhouettes of the mountains. The road shimmered in the heat, and the sand sparkled in the sun.

"What's that?" I asked Glen, as a clump of palm trees appeared in view.

"It's the oasis monastery of the Sacred Heart. It's surrounded by flowering date palms. We'll stop there and buy a Coke."

The orange monastery was Spanish-colonial style. The tall date-palms displayed orange blossoms and provided much-needed shade and rest for our eyes. Only too soon it was time to travel on.

El Vizcaíno turned out to be tiny. All the streets were sand. In the middle of town was a huge sand square surrounded by a stark white Catholic church, a one-room clinic, a two-room elementary school, and an old wooden grocery store. We got out of the truck to stretch our legs and bought another Coke at the store.

"Do you know of anyone who might have a house for rent?" José asked the storekeeper.

"Nope, Señor," he answered, wiping the beer drops from his mustache. "All the houses here belong to the government. Every family is allotted a plot of land and a cottage. If you don't have land, you don't get a cottage. Your only hope is to go door to door and see if someone would be willing to rent you a room."

"This doesn't look good," said Glen, as we climbed back into the truck.

"No, it doesn't," I agreed.

"Oh, have faith, Princess. God will provide," said José, as he always did.

We knocked on several doors. As they opened, we saw simple little rooms, sparsely furnished, often with dirty, half-clad children running about. All the rooms were occupied.

"Doña Juana may have a room," said one of the bare-foot women, who came to the door. She pushed her long hair back from her forehead and balanced her filthy toddler on her hip beside her bulging belly. "Isn't that right, Toño?"

"Si, Señor Profesór. Just follow this road down three more houses, and you'll come to Doña Juana's house. She has the famous baby."

"Famous baby?" I asked.

"Oh, yes, he has miraculous powers!" said Toño. "You'll see."

We made our way to Doña Juana's house. She was short and overweight. Her brown tunic hung loosely over her stocky, braless body.

"I could rent you a room, sure!" she said, leading us into her tiny cottage full of children, dirty dishes, and ironing.

"You'd have to excuse the mess, and of course, you'd have to love children," she said. "In fact, here's the Nene. Everyone calls him my miracle baby. People come from miles around to drink his urine. They swear it makes them well. You mentioned that your wife was sickly, Profesór," she said. "If you want, I can call the Nene right now and give you some of his urine to take with you right away."

"Nene! Nene!" she called to a naked little urchin, who was running around in the dusty yard.

"It's all right, Doña Juana," said José. "We can always come back for the urine. We still have a long way to go."

"Well, let me know about the room. If you get lost, just look for the house that has five pink roses in the front. We brought those in from the mainland. We're very proud of the roses."

"Thanks, Doña Juana. We'll let you know about the room."

"There must be something else," said José, when we had climbed back into the truck. "I just can't have Helenita recuperating from her hepatitis in all that chaos. Besides, it didn't look too clean in Doña Juana's house. Any ideas of what to do now, Glen?"

Glen was silent as we headed toward what looked like a construction site.

"I know they are building an orphanage just outside town. Maybe they can take you in."

The orphanage had only bunk beds and nothing else.

"Look, why don't you stay here for a couple of days. I have to preach on Sunday, but I can come back early in the week and lend you our camper. It's tiny, but it has everything you need. I can set it on the sand next to the Protestant church. I'm sure they won't mind. I've preached there before, and they could probably use a preacher."

"That sounds like a great idea, Glen. Thank you so much," said José, as we unloaded our possessions onto the empty concrete floor of the orphanage.

As Glen had predicted, the church needed a preacher and a pianist, and they were more than happy to let us set the camper in the churchyard in return for our services.

The camper was about eight feet long. It had a raised bed, a table and two bench seats, a small closet, and a stove. It was small enough for me to be able to sweep daily without getting tired. We had a small chamber pot in the camper, and every evening, José would go out under the stars and dig a hole in the sand and empty the contents.

I rested most of the day, except when I went next door to the church and played hymns on the rickety old piano. The solitude and the clean desert air was just what I needed to aid me in my recovery.

José walked to school every day, and on his way home, he stopped at the grocery store to buy food for me. El Vizcaíno was so far from civilization that the only fresh foods were eggs, bananas, and flour tortillas. Canned sardines and mackerel, canned beans and peas, and canned mangoes and peaches were also available. So that is what we ate every day, without exception.

One Sunday we received a visit from Pastor Bello. He was wearing dark glasses, and his wife was driving the station wagon, so we didn't notice at first that Pastor Bello was blind. However, when he stepped out of the car, he was holding a long, white cane.

Pastor Bello told us how he had been blinded in an airplane crash. That had brought him to the Lord, and he now had a church on the west coast of the peninsula. We went to visit him once in the shantytown where he worked. Maybe it was just as well that he couldn't see.

We settled down into a routine in El Vizcaíno. There was no television, no movie theater, no library, no park, no zoo, and no newspaper. Our only entertainment was when the flea market arrived in town, bringing old junk from across the United States border for resale. They had American cars (probably stolen), used refrigerators, used washing machines, and all kinds of used household equipment. Of course they said that everything worked as good as new!

Early in December, José developed a pain in his eye. One of the locals recommended a trip to the Nene's house. José thanked him and went to the local clinic instead. The clinic had two packets of band aids, ten bottles of aspirin, and a few boxes of generic medication. The young intern gave him eye drops and a patch. The pain just grew worse. Finally, the intern told him to go back to La Paz, because an ulcer was perforating his eye.

José bought me some extra cans of food and traveled the fourteen hours by bus to the clinic in La Paz. He returned a few days later.

"They said I have to be evacuated to the mainland, or I'll lose my eye," he said.

"Well, why didn't you go right then?" I asked.

"What? And leave you here all alone in the desert? Come on. We have to pack. We're leaving. They wanted me to fly to Guadalajara, but I told them we have family in Mexico City, so they agreed to give me transfer papers to the government clinic there."

"But we don't have any money," I panicked.

"I've already thought of that. Tonight is the midweek prayer meeting. We brought boxes of toiletries with us from the mainland. Those are very expensive here in El Vizcaíno. What we'll do is set out all the shampoos, perfumes, deodorants, and soaps on the steps outside the church after the service, and let the people know that we have to sell them to raise money for our ticket home."

So we did. The people understood our plight and jumped at the chance to buy our lovely new toiletries at a discount price. We called Glen and asked him to come pick up his camper. José helped him load it on his truck, and then Glen dropped us off at the bus going back to La Paz. The money we had raised was just enough for our bus tickets and some Cokes and tacos on the way.

Once in La Paz, José called his parents, and they wired enough money to pay for our flight out. Just thirteen weeks after our arrival in the peninsula, we were back on the plane to Mexico City.

At least we had escaped the "urine cure!"

CHAPTER 18

As soon as José and I returned to Mexico City, we both caught a terrible flu. We lay in bed for days. Nothing seemed to help. Besides that, our future looked as if it had come to a complete standstill.

We couldn't stay in Mexico City for long because of the pollution. We could not go back to the Baja Peninsula because of José's eye ulcers. We couldn't stay in central Mexico because I didn't do well in the high altitude, and we couldn't go to southern Mexico because it was jungle, and I had had malaria. We seemed to have run out of options.

It was Christmastime, and everyone at the apartment was jolly. José's family was planning a trip to the grandparents' village. They wanted us to get up and go with them. We felt rotten, but they persuaded us to go on the bus with them anyway.

José's grandparents, Abuelito and Abuelita, were pleased to see us again. They asked about Baja. We told them some stories. Uncle Chucho laughed a lot. It seemed like old times again.

"Your Uncle Pedro, who is a preacher in the United States, is home for Christmas," said Uncle Chucho. "He's visiting relatives at the other end of the village, but he says he'll stop by later," said Abuelito.

Presently, Uncle Pedro rolled up in his shiny American station wagon. He was short and chubby with a slick Mexican hairstyle and a long, black Mexican mustache. His wife and children looked us over from head to toe.

"I haven't had the pleasure of meeting your young wife," said Uncle Pedro. I sensed a lurid curiosity. "We're on our way back to Mexico City. Why don't you ride with us?" he said.

José accepted, and we squeezed into the backseat with the children. Uncle Pedro put the car in gear and started down the mud road. At least we wouldn't have to jostle with the Christmas crowds on public transportation while we didn't feel well.

As expected, Uncle Pedro wanted to know all about me. He had never seen a foreign woman with a university education and a raccoon coat in the village before, and he was at a loss to understand why I had married his nephew. I gave him just enough superficial information to satisfy his curiosity, and then José turned the conversation to another subject.

"So, how is life in Texas?" José asked.

"It's great! I'm the pastor of a Spanish-speaking congregation sponsored by a large American church in Corpus Christi," he said. "We're really growing. In fact, we need help. Do either of you know how to play the piano? I'm looking for someone who speaks Spanish to be our youth and music director."

"Helenita plays the piano. She'd be great," volunteered José. Uncle Pablo jumped at it.

So now we were going to Texas, land of oil wells and dry deserts. Not a place I had ever planned to go to, but why not? We had nowhere else to go! We put on our impressive British overcoats and went to the American embassy. They gave us a multiple-entry visitor's visa. If we liked Texas, permanent residency could be obtained later.

Much to my surprise, instead of desert and oil rigs, we found ourselves in lush green countryside. The streets were clean and orderly, and everyone drove in a civilized manner. Even in the quiet suburban streets, the cars would stop at stop signs and politely wait their turn.

We went to a cafeteria that had food much like English food. Everyone spoke English. Everything was so easy. I suddenly realized how hard I had worked to fit into the Mexican culture. I had eaten what they had wanted me to eat, so as not to offend them, even if it made me sick. I had said what they had wanted to hear, so as not to hurt their feelings, even if it wasn't always what I wanted.

Now, all of a sudden, I was free. I could speak English, eat my kind of food, and say what I wanted to say. It felt wonderful. My health was much improved, and I hoped we could stay in Texas forever. Maybe illness had closed the doors on my being a missionary in Latin America, but there was nothing to stop me from being a missionary in Texas!

Uncle Pedro drove us around with him everywhere. When a couple of immigration officers came into the fast-food restaurant to buy a burger, he acted nervous and told us to lower our voices.

"Look out! *La migra! La migra!* Here comes the immigration!" he hissed, looking purposefully down into his plate. We couldn't understand his fears. Maybe when he first came, he might have been an illegal alien, and he wanted us to experience the same fear that he had.

"You have to suffer to deserve the good things in life. You have to pay your dues. I worked hard and long to come to the position I hold now," he said, once the officers had walked out. It was obvious that he had bowed and scraped and manipulated each little circumstance to be able to get ahead. He felt we should have to do the same.

Uncle Pedro organized a welcoming party for us at his church. Many brought gifts: glasses, plates, a few kitchen utensils.

"I want to thank God for bringing us here among such wonderful people," said José, raising his punch glass and smiling. "You have made us feel so very welcome. We look forward to a long and happy relationship working together for the Lord." The people flocked to shake our hands, and their romance with us began.

I started a children's choir. There were some used robes in the storeroom that the mothers were able to shorten. Every Wednesday we practiced some easy songs until they were all in perfect pitch. Then we performed them on Sunday, and the congregation was delighted.

José and I spent time each day, visiting the church families. Many of them were on welfare and could be found at home during the day. We met their children, tasted their food, and listened to their stories.

The youth group started to blossom. Every Sunday we discussed topics relevant to young people. They seemed so naive and unused to discussion. In contrast to the young people in Mexico, they weren't worried about the political situation or the meaning of life. These kids, living mainly in welfare housing, were concerned about their grades and about their peers.

"My parents made all of us kids work as migrant workers in the fields in Michigan this summer, so they could pay Mikey's bail," Flor complained. Her eldest brother, Mikey, was in jail for transporting marijuana across the border. "It's not fair. Why doesn't my mother love us good, hard-working kids? Why does she spend her nights crying for the one bad sheep? She worries more about her bad son being corrupted in jail than she does about us five good kids who need her love and attention!"

Marisa's mother was a widow. Marisa wanted so badly to go to college and be a success to help her mother. But her grades were poor, and she might not be able to make it.

Anita was angry. Her mother was moving them to Houston again. They kept moving back and forth. Anita was angry that her parents divorced. She wanted to be close to her cousins, because they had more fun.

Señora Vallejo was concerned about her daughter, Minerva. Minerva was the middle girl. She didn't seem as bright as her sister, Adriana, nor as outgoing as her sister Elsa. Señora Vallejo was a jolly mother. She cooked and laughed and made sure that everyone in her large family had clean underwear every day.

Delfina Lopez was a diabetic. Her two girls sat quietly, listening as we talked. Her husband, Don Ambrosio, wouldn't come to church, oh, no. But he loved for us to visit and eat his beans. The daughters came and went from the room, obediently bringing whatever the parents asked for. Delfina and Ambrosio wanted their girls to succeed. But living in the housing projects wasn't easy. The government barely gave them enough to eat, but they shared their food gladly, no matter that roaches ran across the table and up our clothes while we talked!

Señor Rodriguez' sixteen-year-old daughter was quiet and sweet. Who knew what lurked behind her smile? His older girl already had a baby out of wedlock. But Señora Rodriguez kept the house spotless and welcomed the boyfriends whenever they came.

"No sense being too legalistic with the girls and running them off," said Señor Rodriguez. He worked at the corner barbershop. He didn't make much money. Their home didn't have air conditioning, but it was always clean and cheerful.

Tina Mayo was distraught. Her children were all wild. Her sons came and went as they pleased. Sometimes they were on drugs. Sometimes they stole or got into trouble. We ate her food too. It made her feel better. The twelve-year-old terrors came by. Their jaded faces already had the looks of criminals. She whined helplessly to us but cursed them aloud whenever they appeared.

Lolita lived with her daughter and son-in-law in a nicer part of town. She had dainty dishes and artificial flowers everywhere. Since there were two working adults in the family, she lived very comfortably. Her granddaughter, Alicia, lacked for nothing, and the Mendoza family contributed a lot to the church. Uncle Pedro visited them all the time. He always asked them for their opinion. But we never saw Uncle Pedro in the government housing projects.

"Why is it that you visit us, and Pastor Pedro doesn't?" we were asked, time and time again in the poorer homes. "Aren't we as important as the people in the nice houses?"

We didn't know how to respond to their questions. Somehow, when we ate their food, it didn't seem to matter anymore. We talked about their kids and about their dreams. And that's all they really cared about.

Our little two-room house was cozy and cheerful. It was a small, wooden house, just the other side of the railway tracks from the nice Anglo houses. A member of the sponsoring church was letting us stay there for a few months. Uncle Pedro and the church members took us back and forth in their cars, since we had no transportation. Some nice ladies from the sponsoring congregation gave us several bags of canned goods, since we weren't allowed to get an income until we were residents.

Uncle Pedro planned a revival week. He always invited a visiting preacher. Someone proposed José, and the congregation voted overwhelmingly in his favor, but Uncle Pedro vetoed the vote.

"Why did you do that?" José asked him, privately. He was furious. "It looks as if you're jealous, and you don't want me to preach in your church. I can understand how you feel, but I think the majority vote should be adhered to. If the pastor can overthrow a majority vote, what is the point of voting in the first place?"

"It's a delicate situation," said Uncle Pedro. He was evasive, but determined, so José backed off. He went to Mexico City to bring back some of our clothes and books.

Uncle Pedro was very solicitous of me during José's absence. He was quick to pick me up and slow to drop me off after church. I had on my suede coat with the raccoon collar, and I sat on the front bench-seat beside him. I could tell he was flattered to have me by his side, and I felt awkward.

"Are you and José happy?" he wanted to know. "Does he treat you well?"

I hesitated.

"Does he beat you?" he asked, intrigued by my silence.

I avoided the question.

"I would be proud to have such a beautiful wife as you," he said. "I'm not so sure that my nephew deserves you. You probably don't know this, but his relatives aren't exactly saints. Oh, no. They have some sex scandals in their past. His Uncle Eduardo ran around on his wife while she was pregnant but you probably didn't know that, did you?"

I was hurt. I didn't want to know any gossip, and his breach of confidence was distressing. I wasn't quite sure what he was going to say next, so I quickly got out of the car and ran into the house.

When José returned from Mexico City, I told him of my conversation with Uncle Pedro. He told me to step closer. Slowly, but intentionally, he pulled off his belt and slashed it across my arms and my legs. Cold, calculated slaps. Like the whippings he had given his twelve-year-old pupils at school.

"I've told you before that you're never to discuss our personal problems with anybody. If you even so much as mention this to anyone, I'll divorce you on the spot," he said.

I was shocked, but I tried not to cry. I felt alone. So very alone. I could not share my heartache with anyone, and once again, I had no place to run.

We started the revival. I gave my list of hymns to Uncle Pedro in advance. Yet every evening, he stood up and announced hymns I had never heard of and had certainly never played before. I stumbled through the hymns, which the congregation didn't know, either, and then I asked him privately why he changed the program.

"I am the pastor," he said. "I have the right to change the program at any time."

"But, Uncle Pedro," I said, "I can't sight-read unknown hymns on the spur of the moment! When you make last-minute changes, I look silly, and the congregation doesn't know the hymns either. They think it's my fault."

"That's your problem," said Uncle Pedro, and walked away.

We went to the board of the sponsoring church. They were shocked. They called Uncle Pedro in. He was defensive, his face as red as a turkey's.

"Either they go, or I go," he said.

"We'll go," José answered. "There's no question about it. We are not interested in a coup to get his church, although this is obviously what he fears. He has a family and depends on the income. We represent a threat to his job security. We'll go."

Plans for José's ordination were accelerated. Once ordained, José could be invited to accept a church of his own, and residency papers would be secured from immigration. As soon as the ceremony was over, the local church hierarchy lined him up with preaching engagements, and an offer of a pastorate was made.

We returned to Mexico City for the remainder of our belongings; now we would reenter the United States as permanent residents.

CHAPTER 19

In January of 1979, we put our canvas wedding portraits in a large straw bag and we flew to Brownsville, Texas. José had been offered his first full-time pastorate in a Spanish-speaking congregation. He was to receive minimum wage, which was about $550 a month, plus parsonage and utilities. He was excited.

Lourdes and Roberto met us at the airport. Lourdes was in her seventies, elegantly dressed, but stooped with age. Roberto was a quiet young man with curly hair and pimples. Together they represented the church treasury and the welcoming committee. They handed the immigration officer a copy of our letter of support, and we were waved into the country without incident.

Lourdes was full of worries.

"We hope you will attract more members, Pastor," she whined. "We need the money badly. Last week they almost turned off the electricity on us. Ever since our last pastor left, things have been pretty bleak."

"Don't worry, Lourdes, God will provide!" said my eternally optimistic husband. "As soon as we get the people organized again and have some prayer meetings, things will get better."

Roberto drove us about four hours north to Corpus Christi, a largely Hispanic city on the coast of the Gulf of Mexico. Near the outskirts of town, he turned into the driveway of the parsonage. It was a chilly day, and as soon as we walked into the little wood-sided house, he showed us how to turn on the heater.

"Just be careful. These gas burners can be dangerous. People have been known to burn to death when these things explode! I live around the corner, and Lourdes lives opposite the church. If you need anything, just come by."

The house was simple, with a small plastic table and chairs in the dining room, a vinyl couch in the living room, and a simple bed in one of the bedrooms. The parishioners had hung a sheet in the window, since the house had no drapes, and someone had put a new bedspread and blanket on the bed.

Meager as these beginnings were, we dropped to our knees and thanked God for the opportunity to be in our very own church and in the United States. We had no car and no furniture, but the church was within walking distance, and we were happy to have a mission again.

Inactive church members came out of the woodwork to check out the new pastor. Forgetting age-old feuds, they packed the pews, eager to give the church a new start. José didn't let them down. His enthusiasm soared to new heights. He was friendly and eloquent and people immediately began to flock to the altar.

Before long, the baptismal font was filled with water, and José was baptizing new believers. He was in his office every day to receive calls and prepare sermons. He took me out each afternoon to visit every family in the congregation. We ate their food, hugged their babies, admired their family portraits and listened to their life stories. I played the piano and the organ, directed the women's society, and worked part time as church secretary a few hours a week.

The church grew. The only problem was that the treasury was in disarray. Roberto counted the money and took it to the bank, and Lourdes signed the checks and paid the bills. Friday was payday, and José walked to Lourdes' house every Friday, hoping to get a paycheck.

"I had to pay the electricity," Lourdes said, self-righteously on José's first payday. "Maybe next week we will have enough for you, but I wouldn't count on it. I had to call the plumber to unstop the sink in the nursery, and he wants his money right away. You know how that goes!"

"But Lourdes, I am your pastor. I have to live."

"Don't look at me, Pastor. There's nothing I can do. All I do is the best I can. What can I do if there isn't enough?"

Every Friday she gave him the runaround. Sometimes he got his paycheck; sometimes he didn't. Things were getting pretty tense around the house. Often we had to make what little food we had last till Sunday and then beg Roberto for some cash to buy a hamburger after the service. A feeling of humiliation started to set in.

One Sunday I was sick and decided not to go to church. I lay down on the sofa and idly turned on the little black-and-white television someone had given us. A religious program was playing. I could hardly believe it. I had never seen a religious program or message on television. I was overcome with emotion as hour after hour, that whole Sunday morning, different Christian programs were aired. Some were just church services, others were special programs where the music was sung in pretty gardens, and the preacher spoke directly into the camera to the viewers at home.

One preacher in particular impressed me with his sincerity and commitment. His name was Oral Roberts, and he was broadcasting from Oklahoma at the crack of dawn. I started to watch his program every Sunday, and soon learned that not only had he built a Christian university, but he was building a hospital where the medical staff would heal the sick and pray for them.

I cried every week when I watched Oral Roberts. He explained that after every harvest season, a farmer keeps his best seed and sows it in the ground to bring forth next year's crop.

"Wouldn't you think it was silly," he said, "if a farmer ran out into the field to see if the crop was growing, if he hadn't first put some seed into the ground?"

He urged us to take our very best seed and plant it in God's work, either in our church, or in his projects. A figure of a thousand dollars popped into my mind. I talked to José about it, and he, generous as always, agreed that we would somehow send a thousand dollars to Oral Roberts to help build the hospital.

As soon as we had sent in our first check, Oral Roberts wrote back to thank us. He urged us to expect a miracle. He told us to pray to God for our needs, and expect Him alone to meet them.

We walked through the house making a list of what we needed. Then we got back down on our knees and laid out the list before God. We needed lampshades, cloth furniture that wouldn't stick to us on hot days, plates, silverware, mugs, glasses, sheets, drapes, clothes, more beds, air conditioning, a car; the list was long, but we said our prayer and waited for God to provide.

When we visited the church members, they usually invited us to stay for dinner. We were so thankful for the free food. In addition, two middle-aged women stopped by our house once a week on their way home from the grocery store. They spent their tithe on groceries and brought them directly to our kitchen. The food they brought was good food—chickens, vegetables, fruit, butter. Because our paychecks were so erratic, it was often the grocery bags of these two unpretentious spinsters that kept us alive.

We both registered for seminary classes nearby and joined the area city choir, rehearsing for a full-blown performance of the Messiah for the following Easter.

We still had no car and no air conditioning. Whenever we needed to go somewhere, we either walked, or relied on someone to come pick us up. But the fierce Texas summer was approaching, and the hot air waves would soon make walking, and even studying at home without air conditioning, impossible.

Just about that time, we received a surprise visit from Brother Tom, who was in charge of the Spanish-speaking churches in our area.

"Brother Bud and Brother Gordon are here from Arkansas," he explained, after we had offered the visitors a seat on our plastic living-room couch.

"We're planning to bring our youth here this summer," said Brother Bud, "and Brother Tom, here, thinks your parsonage could use a little work."

José and I were thrilled. The men examined the failing gas burner, the torn tiles on the floor, the dinginess of the paint, and the lack of air conditioning. They took notes and promised to be back in July.

Just a few weeks later, as we were getting ready for bed, there was a knock on the door. To our amazement, Brother Gordon and his wife had driven in with a truckload of furniture and a used car in tow!

It was just like Christmas! They carried in box after box of gifts from their church members. There were pots and pans, silverware, dishes, clothes, blankets, and drapes. One family sent us two more beds and a beautiful sofa and chair of soft material for the living room. The men promised to return with the youth group and install an air-conditioner unit in the living-room window.

José and I had been sending our checks to Oral Roberts, but not even in our wildest dreams had we imagined that our prayers would be answered so quickly and so specifically. Overnight, our modest parsonage was converted into a comfortable home, and we had a car to drive. All we needed now was the new tile floor, the paint job, and the air conditioning. Soon enough, the youth arrived, and for a week, they swarmed around the parsonage, giving it a total face lift. When they drove away, our home was squeaky clean, freshly painted, and comfortably cool.

Our praise and gratitude to God knew no bounds. Never in my life had I experienced such a dramatic miracle. Oral Roberts had said that it is impossible to outgive God, and he was right. The church was growing, and our personal needs had been met! Wasn't God wonderful!

CHAPTER 20

The next school year was filled with activity. José was invited to appear on a Spanish-speaking program produced at a local television station. At the same time, the church membership had grown so much that we qualified for a denominational loan for the construction of an educational building. The team from Arkansas was going to come back and help us build it.

By now we knew all the families in our church intimately, visiting them regularly in their homes. We always drove up unannounced, so they would not feel obligated to prepare a feast for us; yet they would always eagerly invite us in and beg us to partake of their food. To the Hispanics, as with their ancestors and relatives in Mexico, accepting their food meant accepting them.

"Not even my mother makes such good enchiladas as you do!" José would say.

"Oh, come along now, Pastor," the women would reply, blushing. "It's just my humble cooking!"

"Yes, but it makes me feel so at home," he would continue, thrilling them with his delightful conversation and cheerful manner. He really knew how to make each person feel special and appreciated and I was thrilled to be by his side as our life together blossomed.

We knew who was related to whom, where everyone's unsaved relatives were, what ailments and heartaches they had, and what their dreams for their children were. Some of them stayed in town all year round. Others were unskilled migrant workers who took all their children up north during the summer to harvest the crops. They, in particular, had plenty of time to talk. All of them spoke primarily Spanish, and they felt very comfortable with José and me.

So the church grew, yet the paychecks were still irregular. Week after week, José would return to the house enraged. He felt he had to be polite to Lourdes because of her age, but his frustration with the financial situation was really stressing him. Sometimes, when we had guests for dinner, all I could offer them was scrambled eggs and peas.

The structure of the church did not allow for committees, so the only way we could complain about the treasury would be in front of the whole church at a monthly business meeting. José did not want to embarrass Lupita and Roberto, nor did he want to mention our personal needs in public, so we suffered in silence. The congregation grew, but our refrigerator was often empty, and José became angry inside. At least in Mexico we had had a steady paycheck. Here, we lived at the whim of the Treasurer.

One evening, as we were driving back to the parsonage after dark, José's fury exploded. Just after turning the corner down our street, he started yelling. Without warning, he let go of the steering wheel with his right hand and boxed me on my breast.

I gasped, shocked at the sharp pain. The car jumped the curb and almost ploughed down the parsonage fence. He jerked the wheel and bumped back into the road.

"See what you have made me do!" he yelled. I was horrified. As soon as we got in the house, I ran into the bathroom, locked the door and cried. Then I put the toilet lid down to sit on it and contemplate my situation.

I wanted to call the police and report the incident, but I held back. I was the preacher's wife in a small town. What would this do to the congregation if the whole town knew what had happened? How would Christians in the area react if they read in the front page of the local paper that a preacher had hit his wife and that she had reported him for battery?

What if the police didn't believe me? There had never been any public scandals with preachers or evangelists at that time, and I wasn't brave enough to precipitate the first one. Furthermore, what would I do? I hadn't thought it through well enough. If I were to file charges, his career would be over, and where would that leave me?

"Hurry up and get to bed, woman," José yelled from the bedroom. I flushed the toilet aimlessly, and crept quietly into bed. My breast hurt, but my heart hurt even more.

Not long afterwards, we were due for our first paid vacation, and José was looking forward to returning to Mexico to be with his family. We had been in the United States for a year, waiting for our residence cards to be processed by immigration. They had told us it would take about twelve months and that we could not leave the country before then.

The stress on José during this time had been terrible. All his life, he'd seldom gone a week without seeing his family. Now he went a full year in a completely alien culture, where he barely spoke English and had only survived emotionally because he preached to a Spanish-speaking congregation and ate their homemade Mexican food.

Whereas I had been received with open arms by the Anglo population of Texas because of my "charming" British accent, he struggling with his English, had felt himself to be inferior. Used to being center stage in Mexico, while I served as an ornament and status symbol on his arm, here in Texas, he felt upstaged and out of control.

So long as his congregation admired him, he could carry on, despite his homesickness. But as the financial crisis dragged on, the support systems for his ego were wearing very thin, and I was afraid he could not hold on much longer. He talked daily about his mother, his family, and our upcoming vacation in Mexico City. He was sure our cards would arrive on time, and he rushed eagerly to the mailbox every day, but to no avail.

The year came and went, and the cards never arrived.

"Let's drive to the immigration office in Brownsville to see what the problem is," he said as soon as the one-year deadline had passed.

To his great dismay, the immigration officer said our cards were not ready, and under no circumstances could we exit the United States and ever hope to return.

It was as if a dam had burst. José got in the car and drove all the way home, cursing at the top of his voice. He cursed the immigration officer, the United States, the church, and most of all me.

The Mexicans have a well-developed vocabulary of swear words and insults, but he, being from a good religious family, had never allowed himself to use anything but clean language. That day, his good speech came to an abrupt end. He called me every name under the sun, and I froze to my seat in fear, wondering what would happen next.

José stormed into the house and slammed the door behind him. I didn't know whether to follow and risk another tirade, or to stay in the car and wait till he had calmed down. I decided to sit in the car for a while and cry. It had been all I could do to keep my composure during his spewing of profanity.

I loved him, but I was beginning to wonder if I could continue to live with him. I was afraid of his temper, both physical and verbal. I felt alone and without a future, since my career was tied directly to his. I felt trapped, because I felt I could not tell anyone what I was feeling or going through. Now even my residency status in the United States depended on his job, for without that, there was no way I could remain in the country.

Under no circumstance would I return to my parents, and I couldn't imagine where else I could go. The poverty in which we lived had so undermined my self-confidence that I virtually forgot that I had a degree and was qualified to work in the top international centers of the world. As I roamed the grocery aisles looking for bargains, all I saw were the scrambled eggs and peas we ate so often and the few dollars in my pocket.

After the trip to immigration, José's temper erupted many more times, casting a painful shadow on our relationship. Yet unexpectedly, and in some sick way, it replaced his need to strike me. From then on, whenever he was really angry or frustrated, he exchanged his physical abuses for verbal ones.

Whenever he yelled, I felt such pain and degradation. But the Bible says we should forgive, so I prayed silently that he would change. I never dared stand up to him, because I was afraid he would fall back into old habits and hit me again.

CHAPTER 21

In the late spring, I received an alarming letter from Madeleine. After graduating from Edinburgh, she had moved back down to southern England and was working in London as a translator. In her letter, she told how her father, an established and respected village doctor, had had an affair with his receptionist and had decided to divorce Madeleine's mother.

Madeleine was beside herself with distress. Divorce was almost unheard of in England at that time. Not only was there the scandal to live down, but Madeleine was faced with the disintegration of her family.

"Call her on the phone!" yelled José from the bedroom, when I told him of Madeleine's plight. "Invite her to come and visit us for a few months. That should make her feel better!"

Without thinking, I picked up the phone and dialed Madeleine's number. She said she would resign from her job and be in Texas within the month. In retrospect, I should have stopped to weigh the pros and cons of having a single young woman enter our stormy household, but the deed was done. The die was cast, and Madeleine's arrival was imminent.

Of course, I was thrilled that she was coming. It had been almost three years since I had left Britain, and no one had come to visit me. Now it was time for spring-cleaning the house and getting ready for a visitor!

The car that had been donated to us had finally broken down beyond repair. José and I went into town to purchase a reliable car, so we could have something to drive Madeleine around in.

"This is the best deal I have," said Mr. Conroe, a friend of ours who owned a used-car lot. "It's a little Honda Civic, and it's almost new. The payments are only eighty-three dollars a month."

José and I eagerly looked over the little car. I didn't have my license, because I had never lived in any place where I needed to drive, so José took it carefully around the block.

"The car has no air conditioning," said Mr. Conroe. "That's why the payments are so low."

"Oh, we don't mind," we said, nonchalantly, without realizing that a car without air in Texas was an impossibility.

"Are you sure now?" asked Mr. Conroe.

"Yes, we're sure. We'll take it!" José said, and drove off the lot with the loan papers triumphantly in his hand.

Madeleine looked exotic as she stepped off the plane. She was tall and well groomed, and her expensive clothes flowed gracefully as she moved. She looked as I had only three short years earlier. Now all of a sudden, my simple cotton dress looked so plain, and our little parsonage that we were so proud of seemed so inadequate. Even the car that we had purchased in her honor was tiny.

But Madeleine didn't seem to notice. She was the center of attention, and that suited her fine. We showed her to her bedroom in the back of the house, and she came out and talked with us in the living room, in the coolness of the air conditioning. She had brought some South American records that José was familiar with. He was mesmerized by her, and they talked far into the night, as if intoxicated by one another's company.

"I'm hoping to go to Peru from here," she explained. "I can stay away for several months, and I have brought all my savings; I'm sure I'm going to have a wonderful time here."

We treated Madeleine like a queen and took her everywhere. Only on Fridays, which was our day off to go to the beach, did we leave her at the parsonage alone to fend for herself. She sulked about it.

Every evening I cooked supper for the three of us and then cleaned and washed dishes. Sometimes Madeleine would help me; at other times she would sit and talk to José, who liked to lie on the couch to relax in front of the air conditioning after dinner.

At first, the relationship between the three of us was one of camaraderie, but as time went on, José became more and more intimate with Madeleine and more and more sullen toward me. My feelings were hurt as I felt him pushing me aside, and I prayed desperately for wisdom to know how to behave.

There was a window above the sink in the kitchen, where I often put my silverware to soak. One day I reached to pull out some silverware, and a sharp knife accidentally flew out and landed on my arm, causing a little stab wound in my wrist. I bled profusely and found out later that it had cut through one of my veins.

I asked for prayer at the church and at the seminary, since my wrist hurt when I tried to play the piano. Soon we heard that Uncle Pedro, from our previous church, was circulating a rumor that José and I weren't getting along, and that in desperation, I had tried to slash my wrist and commit suicide. I was horrified and José was furious, but there was nothing we could do except to act happy and hope that the rumor would die down due to lack of fuel.

José became more and more sullen. Often, he would get out of bed and go to the living room. Disturbed from my sleep, I would follow him.

"Go back to the bedroom, woman!" he would order me. "I just want to stretch out in front of the air conditioning. The bedroom is too hot!"

"Fine. I'll lie down beside you here so we can both stay cool," I would say.

"No. Go back to bed!" he would insist. From the tone of his voice, I knew I had to comply. But I couldn't sleep. I would lie on the bed paralyzed, wondering why on earth all of a sudden he wanted to sleep on the living-room floor. The living room was open and easily accessible from Madeleine's bedroom. Every few hours I would get up quietly and peer into the living room. He was always there, but I had a sick feeling in my stomach that wouldn't go away.

To comfort myself, I read the Bible. I pored over the passage that says love believes all things and suffers all things. I talked myself out of my suspicions by telling myself that until I had concrete evidence, I should not jump to wild conclusions and suspect the unthinkable. I struggled to maintain my self-control in the daytime and wept alone on my pillow at night.

"Let's take Madeleine to the Grand Canyon," José proposed one day over lunch.

"Oh, I'd love that!" Madeleine squealed in delight. I went to the bookshelf and pulled out the atlas.

"The trip to the Grand Canyon will take a good three days," I said. "We can only be gone for seven."

"That's not a problem. Madeleine and I can take turns driving," said José.

José arranged for a supply preacher to fill the pulpit, and the three of us took off for the Grand Canyon. That night, we stopped at a little wayside motel outside Big Bend National Park. To save money, someone suggested that we all three share a motel room. There were two large beds and a private bathroom.

It seemed the logical thing to do, so I agreed. It wasn't long though before I had my regrets. In the dark, José kept throwing the covers off of our bed. I kept covering him. Then, to my horror, I awoke to find that he had not only thrown off his covers, but his pajama pants as well. I struggled to put them back on him, and he pretended he was half asleep. It wasn't long before they were off again.

The room was dark, and Madeleine appeared to be fast asleep, but I spent the night in anguish, unable to sleep.

Why was José doing this? I kept asking myself. What was going on? The uneasy feeling in my stomach was growing worse, but what could I say to either one of them? They weren't doing anything wrong.

Or were they?

At Big Bend National Park, we jumped out of the car and walked over the big round stones and through the deep desert canyon to touch the cool, rippling water of the Rio

Grande. As we made our way back to the car, José suddenly took us each by the hand. I was furious, but I bit my lip. I couldn't believe what he was doing, but I didn't want to cause a scene. Later I told him how angry I was, and he acted remorseful.

During the rest of the trip, José and I usually slept in the tent, and Madeleine in the car. One more time we stayed at a motel, but it was cheap, and at my insistence, we got separate rooms.

All the way back to Texas, I sat in the backseat, pondering the situation, while José and Madeleine chatted merrily in the front and took turns driving. I was beginning to feel very much out of control, and decided that as soon as we got back home, I would take lessons and get my driver's permit.

My instructor had a little car like mine, so she would come and get me and take me to a deserted parking lot to practice three times a week.

Whenever I returned from my driving lessons, I would find José sitting on the sofa reading, and Madeleine in the bathroom, showering. I didn't give it much thought, although somewhere in my subconscious mind, it did register that Madeleine was always in the bathroom whenever I got home, and she always stayed in there a very long time. I justified that by reminding myself that Madeleine had always taken her time in the bath, but my subconscious seemed to suggest that she hadn't been in the bathroom long whenever I pulled into the driveway.

In the meantime, José kept sleeping on the floor of the living room, and I would get up periodically to make sure he was still there. He always was. My mind told me, *See. What are you worrying about?* My intuition said, *There is something fishy going on here,* but I couldn't seem to put my finger on it.

One of the nicest people in our congregation was Consuelo, a single mother. She was petite with big brown eyes and bleached blond hair. She lived in a mobile-home park outside town and had two small children, each by a different father. Whenever Consuelo was in town shopping, she would stop by with the two little boys. José was crazy about the boys, and whenever we drove east of town, we would go and see her.

Consuelo started to attend church regularly and even volunteered to help in the nursery. She prayed the prayer of salvation and hoped to be baptized soon.

One afternoon, three of the elderly women came to the parsonage looking very glum.

"We have a serious problem, Pastor," said Benita, the spokeswoman. "We heard that Consuelo has taken her two little boys and moved in with a man, and they are not married. We don't think she should be teaching nursery school."

José tried to be diplomatic and agreed to visit Consuelo to find out what was going on. I went with him the next day to see Consuelo's new house. She welcomed us and looked embarrassed as José stepped over a man's pair of shoes in the hallway.

"Look, Consuelo," preached José, "the Bible is against fornication and immorality. You need to make a decision. Either you marry the guy or move out, or else the church board will have to make a decision."

Consuelo cried and didn't do anything. The matter was brought before the board at the monthly business meeting. Consuelo's sin was publicly denounced. She was fired from teaching in the nursery and not allowed to participate in communion.

I was stunned, and Consuelo stopped coming to church. Her children ran wild and never appeared in any of the Vacation Bible Schools again.

Meanwhile, a letter came from immigration allowing us to return to Mexico, so José immediately took a leave of absence, and invited Madeleine to fly down with us. In his eagerness to see his family, he had not even considered whether there would be room for her in his parents' tiny apartment.

"The girls can put newspaper down on the tile floor in the hallway and give Madeleine their room," said my mother-in-law. "And the boys can sleep on the sofas in the living room. That will leave one bedroom for me and my husband, one for José and Helen, and one for Madeleine."

I was shocked at the number of people who would have to be displaced to accommodate the three of us, so I made a stupid suggestion.

"Madeleine can sleep in our bed. I'll sleep in the middle, and that way your sisters and your brothers won't have to give up their bedrooms and sleep on the floor."

"Are you sure about that?" said my mother-in-law, looking at me suspiciously.

"Oh, yes. We'll be fine," I said, signing my own death warrant. Madeleine went with us everywhere, even to bed.

One evening, as I approached our bedroom door, Madeleine reached for the door handle, but I stopped her.

"Wait a minute, Madeleine," I said, "José hasn't finished changing." I knew he was under the sheets naked, as I had just gone out to get him a clean pair of pajamas.

"No," Madeleine said, pushing me away. "I need to talk to him in private."

"You can't go in just yet," I said, holding onto the handle tightly.

"I need to talk to him," she said, "privately." She pushed past me aggressively and opened the door. José was lying naked under the sheets. She went in and closed the door behind her.

I stood outside the door seething for a couple of minutes. On the one hand, I wanted to kill her. On the other hand, my strong British upbringing compelled me not to cause a scene.

Finally, I could stand it no longer. I opened the door to the bedroom and went in. Madeleine was sitting on top of the sheets, talking to José. He was lying under the sheets, listening.

"Please come outside for a minute," I asked Madeleine, leading the way to the outdoor washroom, where the day's laundry was hanging on the lines to dry. Madeleine followed me, and I turned to face her.

"Look, Madeleine!" I hissed. I was in such a rage that I wanted to claw her eyes out. "I've given you my car, my house, my vacations, my food, and my money, but I will *not* give you my husband!"

My eyes must have burned like fire. Madeleine was shocked, and neither of us said anything for the rest of the day.

Not long after we returned to Texas, José came home to get Madeleine and drove her to the church office. Two hours later, he brought her back, and she started packing. The next day, we drove her to the airport, and I never saw her again.

"What happened to Madeleine?" I asked José, when I saw her packing her things.

"I took her to my office and told her that if things continued the way they were going, I would lose you, and I wasn't prepared to do that. So I told Madeleine she had to go."

Relieved, I put Madeleine out of my mind, and strived to rebuild a normal home life. At least I was alone with José again, instead of being miserable in our *ménage à trois!*

CHAPTER 22

After Madeleine left the house, I expected life to bounce back to normal, but it didn't. Our financial situation continued to deteriorate. We had a new treasurer now, but even he was not able to pay us regularly, and almost every Sunday we had to beg for a few dollars to be able to eat. Sometimes, when we had eaten all the groceries the two sisters had given us, all we had left were a couple of Cokes and some sweet bread that the owner of the bakery gave us.

Someone sent us a box of used clothing. I unpacked it to find a bra with torn elastic and soiled underwear. Being the recipient of such a donation was worse than humiliating. Things were looking pretty bleak.

I kept wondering what had gone awry. Why had we experienced such dramatic blessings on our arrival at the church and seemingly nothing but curses now? I knew what the peace and blessing of God felt like, and I knew that we didn't have them. I struggled to find the missing piece of the puzzle, while at the same time, the cloud of financial difficulties grew darker and darker.

Finally, José went to see Brother Tom at the denominational offices. We had read that there was a tremendous shortage of Spanish-speaking preachers in California, and the denomination was recruiting heavily in its shiny magazines. In fact the whole missions thrust for that year was California, which they said, was crying out for hundreds of ethnic pastors.

"We can't hang on much longer," José told Brother Tom. "We haven't been paid on time in weeks. We have to make our car payment so that we don't ruin our credit, but after that, we often go hungry. I've talked to the treasurer about it several times, but it hasn't seemed to help. I don't know what else to do!"

Brother Tom obliged by writing a recommendation to San Diego, and we soon received a warm letter of welcome from Dr. Stephens, the director of pastoral staff for the city. He said that all we had to do was to get there, and José would be assured of a choice of pastorates.

There was nothing left but to sell all our worldly belongings. I wept as we put up garage sale signs and pulled all the furniture and household goods the people from the church in Arkansas had so generously given us out onto the lawn for all passersby to see.

I was ashamed that we were having to sell God's blessings just to eat. I felt we were betraying the goodness of those who had just so recently sacrificed so that the work could continue. Yet at the same time, our salaries were weeks behind, our car payment had to be made, and we had to eat.

Maybe if we had told the church members just how desperate we were, they would not have let us go. But we were too proud to admit our total poverty and too kind to embarrass the treasurers in public. So José gave the typical pastoral speech about "God calling him to California, and how, with great regret, he would have to leave this place." The people cried, and we cried too. Then we locked the door behind us and drove away.

We had our clothes, our wedding portraits, and our books packed tightly into our little Honda. We decided to take the long way to California and visit the Indian territories of Oklahoma and Arizona for a little vacation. We hoped that our problems would become a thing of the past, and we would arrive in California refreshed and enthusiastic again.

True to form, José bounced back to his usual romantic and optimistic self as we drove along the great American highways in search of our fortune out west! We had enough money to stay in little roadside motels, visit local sites, and generally have a wonderful vacation.

José assured me that our financial worries were all in the past. In California, we would find our destiny. We would be welcomed and appreciated, and his preaching career would take off again. We would build and grow and touch many peoples' lives. After all, California was the melting pot with Asians, Africans, and Europeans added to the Hispanic and Anglo mix that we were already used to. He sang and whistled happily as we drove, and I laughed and fell in love with him all over again.

Much to our surprise, however, California was more chaotic than we ever imagined. Without warning, we found ourselves on a highway with eight lanes flowing in one direction and eight in another direction.

Dr. Stephens, the denominational representative, welcomed us to San Diego and invited us stay in his garage apartment while we found a church. Much to our shock and dismay, however, he only had two Spanish-speaking congregations available.

One consisted of thirty people who were sharply divided. It offered $300 a month and no parsonage or living expenses. The other was an extended Mexican family and their friends, a group of twenty people headed by a little old matriarch. They offered $250 a month, also without parsonage. Minimum wage was $550 and renting was far more expensive than in Texas. Neither congregation allowed the pastor to hold down a secular job.

"How are we supposed to make ends meet?" we asked, stunned.

"The wife is expected to work, of course," he said, matter-of-factly.

José and I were crushed. For all these years, we had worked together in the ministry, our strength lying in our home visitation program. If I had to go to work, we would only be able to visit people on a limited basis, and José would have a lot of free time on his hands.

We didn't know what to do. We visited both congregations and preferred the second one. We discussed our decision for days. California was a far cry from rural Texas. People were not as supportive as we had experienced in Texas. We felt quite alone. But there was no turning back. If nothing else, we were almost penniless. We would have to make a go of it.

The California traffic sped by us as we drove along the endless, fast-moving highways in a daze. Life here was lived in the fast lane, one fad entering as quickly as another was exiting. Fabulous homes were perched on hillsides on the San Andreas Fault, destined to be ripped into the ocean with the next earthquake. People of all races and walks of life raced by each other, or passed fleetingly at the gas-station quick shops. Everyone was looking out for Number One. Nobody had time to talk. Nobody who had productive things to do, that is. However, in the Mexican congregation, where José finally agreed to serve, was Señora Ramos, the self-appointed matriarch. She was constantly inviting us to her house for Mexican dinners and briefing sessions. She hoped that José would preach on exactly the topics that she had in mind and that his position on each issue would be identical to hers.

The big Anglo church sponsoring the Hispanic congregation put us in touch with a retired lady who had a mobile home. She wanted us to house-sit for three months while she went out of town. We were thrilled to accept her offer and save on rent.

Having settled into our new temporary home, I searched the papers for a job as an interpreter or translator. There were none. So after pounding the pavement for a couple of weeks, I accepted a position as a bilingual secretary in a yacht exporting company not far away, and we decided to make the best of a bad situation.

Things could only get better, or so we thought!

CHAPTER 23

When our three months of house-sitting ended, we moved into an unfurnished apartment close by. We didn't have any furniture as yet, so when old Mrs. Brandon called from the retirement village and said she had a sofa for us, we were delighted.

"I'll get it while you are at work today," José yelled, as I was putting on my makeup in the bathroom. A sofa was a start. We hoped a table and chairs would be forthcoming soon.

That morning, the office door suddenly burst open, and my boss at the yacht company staggered in drunk. He hit the back of my chair, uttering obscene comments. Frightened, I picked up my purse and walked out. I would just have to look for another job after Christmas.

Another family from the sponsor church asked us to house-sit for them over the holidays. We told them we had just rented an apartment but we would be glad to check on their house daily. We went to the Wilson's house every evening. They had a television, which we didn't have, so it was nice entertainment. Then we would drive home and sleep on the floor in our apartment where the carpet was still moist from being shampooed.

For Christmas eve, the young Ramirez family invited us for a simple meal with their children, so we would not be alone. We didn't have a phone yet, and we didn't want to use the Wilsons', so we asked Deacon Brody at the Anglo church if we could call our families in London and Mexico City on the church phone on Christmas day. We promised to pay him back when the phone bill arrived.

Deacon Brody unlocked the church office and waited while we made the calls. This was our first Christmas away from both families. The cheerful voices on the other end of the phone made us feel ever more homesick as we drove back in the bitter cold to our empty apartment.

One evening, while at the Wilson's, we both started to feel very feverish. It was bitterly cold outside and raining heavily.

"It's still pouring," said José, peeking through the curtains at the interminable rain. "I don't think the Wilsons would mind if we spent the night. After all, they did invite us to stay here and sleep in their bed."

"I think that's a good idea," I said. "If we get to feeling much worse, we couldn't even call for help, since we don't have a phone in our place yet."

It was late, it was dark, and it was cold. The drive back to our empty apartment would have exposed us to the elements, and the Wilson's bed was so inviting. We decided to spend the night. The following morning, we went to see the doctor. We both had a high fever, and my breasts were oozing pus. I thought we had some virulent flu strain.

The nurse at the clinic sent José down one hall and took me to an empty room down another. After the preliminary paperwork was done, she told me to disrobe and wait for the doctor.

I sat patiently on the table in my paper-thin robe. It wasn't long before the doctor arrived.

"What is going on with you, young lady?" he chirped.

"I have a fever, and my breasts are oozing pus," I said.

"OK. Let's have a look," he said, pulling away my gown.

"Ho! ho! ho! What have we here?" the doctor said, half seriously, half jokingly. "Who has your husband been sleeping with?"

"What do you mean?" I asked. I didn't know whether to slap him across the face for his impudence or take him seriously. "My husband is a minister! He hasn't been sleeping with anybody!"

"Well, minister or not, my dear young lady," the doctor continued in his semisarcastic manner, "you have a flaming case of syphilis! I'm going to give you some prescriptions, but they will do you no good unless your husband also takes medication. I'll examine him and make sure he gets some prescription medicine also. There's a pharmacy down the hall, and you need to both come and see me in about a week. . . ."

I wasn't paying any attention to him. My face was hot and flushed with embarrassment. I was furious that he would even make such a blatant accusation. It was clear that he didn't know what he was talking about! How could I possibly have syphilis? That was a sexually transmitted disease! I had heard about it in connection with prostitution, but we were in the ministry, and I certainly wasn't going to give credence to any such wild claims.

"You wouldn't believe what the doctor asked me!" I said to José in amusement, as we left the clinic reception. "He wanted to know who you had been sleeping with. He claims we both have syphilis! Did he examine you?"

"Yes. He told me the same thing. I don't know what he's talking about. All I know is that I feel lousy, and I want to go back to bed. The problem is, we don't have the fifty-five dollars it takes to buy the prescription medication, so we may as well go back to the Wilsons and see about the prescription later."

We called our friends, the Ramirez family, and told them we were ill. We asked if we could borrow fifty-five dollars for our prescription. They said they didn't have that kind of money, but they called Deacon Brody at the sponsor church. He came to the Wilson's to get us and took us to the pharmacy to get the medicine.

"We're sorry we put you to all this trouble in the middle of the Christmas holidays, Brother Brody, but we feel terrible, and we didn't have the money for this. We really appreciate it. We should get paid on the thirty-first, so we'll pay you back then."

I was embarrassed to be standing in the pharmacy with a church deacon who was going to hand over the cash directly to the pharmacy to make sure we got our syphilis medication. That was even more embarrassing than the ridiculous allegation that the doctor had made about José! I wished we could hurry back to bed and get this fever over with.

That took a few days, so we just tossed and turned in the Wilson's bed. We slept constantly, except when it was time to water the plants, or take another dose of medication.

"Oh, my God," I said one morning when I woke up and looked at José. One side of his face was completely paralyzed. He blinked one eye, while the other remained open.

"Quick, I'll call Brother Ramirez. We have to get you to a doctor."

"Rudy," I stammered, as soon as he picked up the line. "Something terrible has happened. Half of José's face is paralyzed! We're both too sick to drive. Would you come and take us to the doctor?"

I tried to be brave as we staggered into our clothes and waited for Rudy to arrive. When he stepped into the house and saw José, he was horrified.

"What happened, Pastor?"

"I don't know," said José. "I've been on medication fighting this fever for several days, and today I woke up paralyzed."

"Can you smile? Can you close your mouth? Can you do anything?"

"No," said José, "I can't."

His speech was slurred, and one eye wouldn't blink at all. He tried to swallow some coffee, but it fell out of his mouth because he couldn't bring his lips together.

Rudy sat down with us and prayed.

"Oh, God," he pleaded, "please let the doctor find out what the problem is with Pastor José. We need him to keep preaching. He needs his health back. Please bring help soon."

We piled into Rudy's car and went back to the clinic for a diagnosis.

"You have Bell's palsy," the doctor said. "There is no cure. You're just going to have to hope and pray it goes away."

"How long could that take?" I said, horrified.

"Some people have it for a few days; with others, it can take months."

"But he will eventually get well, right?" I asked.

"Hopefully. But there are no guarantees."

We drove back to the Wilson's in silence. We were too sick even to understand the implications, yet optimistic enough to hope that in a few days, our nightmare would be over. Rudy dropped us off, and we tumbled back into bed.

The next time we awoke, it was the middle of the night.

"Shhh!" José was whispering. "Somebody has just driven into the driveway! I'm going to the window to take a look."

He pulled back the curtain.

"It's the Wilsons! They're back from Mississippi!"

"Oh, no! They weren't due back for another couple of days, and they don't know we are in here! I'll run and warn them, or they might think we are intruders and shoot us!"

I ran down the hall toward the front door in a panic. We were in a sorry mess. The dishes weren't washed, there were a couple of opened sardine cans on the coffee table, our clothes were lying around, and we were asleep in their bed! I was afraid to turn on the light and startle them. On the other hand, I was afraid not to turn on the light, since they might mistake me for a robber.

It was too late, anyway. The key was turning in the keyhole. Mrs. Wilson's shadow appeared in the open door.

"Mrs. Wilson, it's me, Helen!" I called out, sheepishly. Just then, the light turned on, and we stood facing one another in shock.

"What are you doing here?" she said in disbelief.

"We took ill one night while watching your television, so we decided to stay on because we don't have a bed or a telephone in our apartment. José is in your bed, and his face is paralyzed. We didn't expect you back today. . . . "

Mr. Wilson had stepped in by now.

"What on earth is going on here?" he asked gruffly, as he saw a worried Mrs. Wilson talking to me in my nightie by the kitchen sink.

"I'm so sorry the place is a mess. We've been so sick, and we didn't expect you back so soon."

"It's OK, dear," said Mrs. Wilson, trying her best to remain both calm and kind at three o'clock in the morning, after a long, hard drive. "Why don't you just go back to bed. We'll crash on the sleeper sofa here in the living room, and we'll straighten everything out in the morning."

The following morning, the Wilsons were so touched by our plight that they insisted that we stay on for one more night. Then they helped us move back to our apartment, arranged for us at least to get a mattress, and our medical bills paid.

The doctor told José to tape his paralyzed eye shut since it refused to blink and wouldn't lubricate. He also prescribed some eyedrops to keep the paralyzed eye moist.

Eating was difficult for José, but drinking was impossible. One side of his lip closed, but the other side was limp. Drinks drooled down his face. His speech was impaired too. One half of his mouth functioned and mouthed words perfectly. The other half of his mouth was out of control and distorted any sound his good half made. For a man who made his living by preaching, he was in a serious predicament.

It was time to take a grim, hard look at reality. We were living in an apartment, empty except for a donated sofa, a table, two chairs, and a mattress. José had to cancel all his preaching engagements. I had quit my job. What little money came in on December 31, paid off our bills. We missed Texas and had no compelling reason to stay in California.

When all we had left was just enough to buy a large bag of peanuts to eat and enough gas to drive to Texas, we vacated our apartment and climbed back into our little Honda. José put a fresh patch on his eye, and we took turns driving for two days straight. We didn't stop to rest on the way, because we had no money for a motel.

When news of our departure reached Dr. Stephens, he wrote us a lengthy reprimand for being irresponsible. He mentioned the long distance calls from the church phone and the empty sardine cans on the Wilsons' coffee table.

I was devastated.

CHAPTER 24

We had called some close friends in Corpus Christi to let them know we were heading back, but when we knocked on their door at dusk, they said they were sick and couldn't invite us in. They had no idea that we had eaten peanuts for two days, and our stomachs were growling with hunger pangs. They said they had arranged for us to stay in a mobile home at a nearby youth camp and told us how to get there in the dark.

The camp was a few miles out of town and off the beaten track. We found the caretaker, and he showed us to a mobile home, empty except for a bed and table. He told us that the heating didn't work, and there was no shower. He said we could use the cold shower in a concrete shed a couple of hundred yards away, and he bid us goodnight.

We weren't sure whether to laugh or cry.

José's eye was still taped shut, and he couldn't talk or eat normally. Brother Tom at the denominational offices said there was nothing the denomination could do for us until José was able to preach again, so we had no alternative but to drive to the government food-stamp office. Not only was it humiliating, but we found out that it took six weeks before welfare benefits took effect.

"I can't believe that the government has no program for crises!" I told José, as we drove away in despair. "I wonder how other destitute people survive for six weeks! We need emergency help now! In six weeks we'll probably have a job."

José called home to Mexico City, and his parents sent us enough money to buy food for a couple of weeks.

"I hate to keep taking money from your family every time we have a crisis," I said.

"They're great, aren't they? I'm so thankful for the support they give us. But God will provide, Princess. Don't worry," said José, as he always did. "Be grateful that we have a roof over our heads. Something'll come along, you'll see."

What came along was an opportunity to sell costume jewelry, while I looked for a real job. The leads in the local paper proved to be worthless, but I did see several positions advertised by an employment agency. So I put on my nice suit and took the elevator to their office on the sixth floor of the downtown bank.

While I was being interviewed, a small, blonde lady called my counselor away.

"That was Debbie, the owner," she said when she returned a few minutes later. "I think she likes the sound of your English accent. She says you're obviously not afraid to talk, so she wants to offer you a job here!"

"What kind of a job?" I asked.

"As an employment counselor! You will interview applicants and then call around in the community to set up job interviews for them. As you build up your clientele, employers will call you with job openings, and you can often fill them with applicants you already have in your files. It's kind of fun, and you meet a lot of nice people."

"How much would I be making?" I asked.

"Everyone is paid a base of minimum wage, and then you make commissions depending on how well you do. You can do very well if you work hard."

As I walked back to the elevator, I felt a sense of excitement. Granted, it wasn't what I would have been making as an interpreter in Brussels, but it was work, and I was in the United States. I had an opportunity to learn a new career in a lovely office with the possibility of commissions too. God knew we had to have immediate income, and maybe this was just what I needed.

"Here is the company manual," said Debbie when I arrived at work the next day. "I want you to read it carefully. We are a franchise, and if you do exactly what the manual says, you will succeed. We have contests and prizes and all kinds of fun here, but first, you must read the manual."

Since I was already in the habit of reading the Bible and doing what it said, I had no problem with reading the manual and following it to the letter. Debbie came by to quiz me every once in a while and seemed pleased with my progress.

"Here is your first application. I want you to make calls and get an appointment for this young woman. She was a cheerleader in high school and had a 3.5 GPA in college."

What was a cheerleader? And what was GPA? And was 3.5 good or bad? I had no idea. When I asked Debbie, she laughed. Business immediately ground to a halt as the other counselors gathered around in amusement to explain to me the idiosyncrasies of the American language.

"So what is chicken-fried steak?" I asked them. "I ordered it in the restaurant the other day, and they didn't bring a filet of chicken breast at all!" The women laughed. "Biscuits are cookies, muffins are biscuits, and English muffins are crumpets. I never know what I'll be getting!"

"OK, girls. Let's get back to work," Debbie said, finally. Turning to me, she continued, "Just pick up the phone and start calling. You have to learn by doing."

Once I started to interview applicants myself, it became much easier to promote them in town. I continued to follow the exact words in the book, and much to my surprise, I started placing people and logging commissions in my calendar. In addition, our finances were further bolstered when I unexpectedly received a $10,000 check from my grandmother's estate. It couldn't have come at a better time.

Since my initial travels across the United States, I had dreamed of owning a mobile home. They seemed so American and so novel. I had spent a lot of time camping as a child, and a mobile home represented one glorified vacation. José and I could not live in the camp indefinitely, so I put a down payment on an acre of land in the country and paid cash for a brand-new mobile home.

José and I were ecstatic. He supervised the digging of the septic tank, the well, and the installation of the mobile home while I was at work. He did the grocery shopping and put the dirty dishes in the dishwasher. Before long, he was able to talk again, and he picked up some substitute preaching. We hoped that before the year was out, he would be able to get a preaching job again and everything would be all right.

We bought a used, rust-colored Mercury Cougar with air conditioning for me to drive to work. We also bought a couple of dogs and took them for walks in the early morning dew. When my Irish setter had eight puppies, I treated them as babies and sat them on the hood of the car for a family photo. I was so happy. The golden sunflowers surrounding our mobile home were in full bloom. José's eye was improving, and his lip was on the mend too. My commissions were growing from month to month, and it looked as if we would finally have some stability in our lives.

"Here is a contest, Helen," said Debbie. "Nobody in this part of the country has ever made it, but we're working on it. I thought you might like to give it a try!"

I had no doubt in my heart that I would win the contest. I took the pamphlet and hung it on the corkboard in front of my desk. Month after month, silver and gold achievement certificates with my name on them poured in from corporate headquarters, and just a few days before the deadline, I won!

Debbie was delighted, and my income skyrocketed.

CHAPTER 25

Since we lived in the country, José rented a mailbox. He insisted on coming into town every day to pick up the mail himself, even though I worked only two blocks away from the mailbox.

One day while he was out of town, I went to the mailbox to see what had come in. I found a note covered with hearts and kisses from a lovesick young teenager who had come to paint the parsonage with the youth group from Arkansas. When I questioned José about it, he was furious with me for going to the mailbox in the first place. He said the young girl probably had a crush on him and forbade me from ever going to the mailbox again.

I called José's mother in Mexico City to ask her opinion about the love note. She told me it was probably nothing to worry about.

"You know how it is, Helenita. Boys will be boys!"

I wasn't convinced.

A few months passed, and José's face healed well enough for him to interview again for the pastorate. We were called to another small town that provided an ample parsonage for the two of us and our dogs. We kept the mobile home in the orchard as a security, and I kept my job as an employment counselor, because I loved it and was doing very well.

After we had been at the parsonage for several months, God spoke to me early one morning. It startled me a great deal, because God didn't usually speak to me that clearly. I usually read a passage of Scripture every morning, thought about it for a while, and then prayed that I could apply it in my life. But this was different. God told me very clearly that today I would encounter an obstacle. It would seem very big to me, but all I had to do was to step over it, for it would be no bigger than a speed bump.

I was intrigued. A speed bump didn't seem big at all. What would happen today that would be an obstacle, and why did God have to warn me about it?

I showered, put on my dark green suit, rust colored blouse, matching shoes, and makeup. Then I got into my rust-colored, air-conditioned, Mercury Cougar. The big lawn outside the parsonage was wet with dew, and the trees outside the church were green. I drove past the brick sign announcing this Sunday's sermon with the name, Reverend José Mendez, Pastor, in big letters at the bottom. The church was all locked up, and there wasn't a soul in sight.

I turned right past the old brick courthouse, went over the tracks, and down First Street. The old cinema had a letter falling off its sign, and the new bank had two cars in the parking lot. The dime-store lot was still deserted, and in the breakfast taco place, several workers sipped hot coffee before the day began.

The freeway to work was straight and empty. Fields of corn and sunflowers were on either side. Every few miles or so, I would pass a small town with its cotton gin, silo, and railroad cars. I put the Cougar into cruise control. I loved to do that. It made me feel so American, so modern. I could put my feet on the floor and just enjoy the music.

I reached Corpus in perfect time, drove down Main Street, and turned into the bank's parking lot. I took the elevator and arrived at the office door just as Debbie was opening up.

"Lovely morning," I said, as I made my way to my desk and reached in the drawer for my dark red nail polish. My spending the first few minutes of each day putting on nail polish annoyed Debbie, but since I was her star performer and didn't spend time on coffee breaks, she didn't make an issue of it. My desk was right by the window, and through the blinds I could see the neat little neighborhood sprawled out below and the morning sun glistening on the rooftops.

I wondered, as I painted my fingernails, what could possibly go wrong at the office today. I had several people out on interviews and a few offers in the works, but the unexpected could always happen. Every once in a while, I remembered the morning warning, but things were running pretty smoothly, so by lunchtime I decided not to worry about it.

At noon I headed back down the elevator to the car. The local manager of E. F. Hutton got in the elevator, her string of pearls swaying across her expensive blouse. "When E. F. Hutton speaks . . ." The words of the television commercial rang in my ears. The doors closed, and the elevator began to move.

"Going anywhere special for lunch today?" she asked.

"No. Just the usual trip to the health-food store. I'm trying to cut down on the beef, so the health food will do fine," I replied.

The car was like an oven in the noonday Texas heat. I turned on the air conditioning and cruised back down Main, past the quaint little wooden houses converted into chic gift shops. At the dead end, I turned left and headed straight for the health-food store. In the refrigerated section, I found my favorite cookie, made of natural ingredients, of course, with blueberry ice cream sandwiched in the middle. I paid and sat down at one of the little tables to enjoy my delicacy.

After the cookie was gone, I threw the silver paper into the trash and browsed through the book section until it was time to go back to work.

I was absorbed in several intricate negotiations, so the afternoon passed quickly. One client took a job, and an engineer that I had been trying to recruit for an oil and gas company in Wyoming, agreed to send me his resumé. Debbie had to run an errand, and Dawn got a lead on a new sales job with Nabisco. One of my most loyal employers placed an order with me, and a retirement home called, wanting to hire a bookkeeper I had just sent out. When closing time came, it caught me quite by surprise.

I grabbed my purse and car keys and got on the elevator with Debbie and Dawn. We made small talk as we went down. The people at E. F. Hutton were bent over the boss's desk, engrossed in some serious discussion as we passed by.

We opened the door to the outside, and the heat hit us like a blast furnace.

"Bye. See you tomorrow!" we called out to each other. I had just started walking toward my Mercury when I noticed José in our little Honda, waiting for me. Strange. What was he doing in town?

"Hop in," he said.

"How come you're in town today?" I asked, surprised.

"Oh, I needed to talk to you about something, so I decided I'd just swing by and pick you up."

"Do you want to go to the pizza parlor, and then come back for my car?" I asked. Sometimes he would whisk me off to the all-you-can-eat pizza buffet, so I wouldn't have to cook and wash dishes.

"No. Let's just drive home. I can bring you back to work tomorrow morning."

My curiosity was aroused. What was going on? He put the car into gear and drove out of the bank's parking lot.

"Did you go to the seminary classes this morning?" I asked.

"Yes, I did. And that's what I wanted to talk to you about. I went to the seminary, but I didn't enroll in the classes."

"Why not?" I asked, surprised.

"Well, that's what I wanted to talk to you about."

I was intrigued. He was going round and round in circles, and I wanted to know what was going on.

"You remember I went to that religious convention a couple of weeks ago?" he continued.

Instantly, I felt a stab in my heart. This was it. I knew it. He was about to give me some bad news, and for an instant, I was emotionally paralyzed. I remembered God's word from that morning, and took a deep breath. I had to stay calm. Whatever it was, I could handle it. All I had to do was to step over it, just as if it were a speed bump.

"Yes," I said, turning to face him, as he drove over the railroad tracks and onto the freeway. He was wearing sunglasses, and the skin on his cheeks seemed particularly red and irritated.

I remembered when he had called me from a pay phone just a couple of hours after leaving for the convention.

"The roads are flooded and there are flash-flood warnings everywhere!" he had yelled over the sound of the pouring rain.

"Don't let that stop you!" I had said. "You've planned for this trip for so long. Just go for it. You'll be fine!" I had let him borrow my camera so he could take pictures of the convention speakers.

"Dr. Brown and Brother Tom called me into their office first thing this morning, so I missed the classes," José was saying.

"What did they want?" I asked, bracing myself. A sick feeling in the pit of my stomach had come over me, and I felt slightly dizzy. I remembered the pictures that had come back from the photo shop after José's return from the convention. Women. Women at the hotel pool. Women in swimsuits. The backsides of women in swimsuits.

"What is this?" I had said horrified, as I had opened the packet of photographs.

"Oh, just some people at the pool at the hotel. I was practicing with your camera."

"Practicing on the backsides of women?" I had asked.

"Oh, that's nothing. They were just lying around the pool."

I had secretly called his mother in Mexico City right away, hoping she would give me some support. José was a big believer in keeping our own counsel, but I had been so shocked that I needed to confide in her.

"Oh, Helenita," she had said. "You know how men are. I'm sure it doesn't mean anything." Somehow, I hadn't been convinced.

José swallowed hard and started to speak again: "While I was at the convention, I was caught with a girl."

A knife stab in my heart would have been more bearable. Everything I knew and trusted seemed to suddenly leave me. I was heading into the unknown, and I was terrified.

"What happened?" I asked.

"We didn't go all the way," he said, trying to justify himself.

"So what *did* you do?"

"There was a girl in the choir. She and I started talking. One thing led to another. You know how it goes. Anyway, they caught us petting in one of the empty rooms at the convention. She had to go back out and sing with the choir afterward, and she broke down during the performance. Everyone crowded around to ask her what had happened, and she was hysterical."

"Well, did you try to rape her?"

"No. She went along with everything. They just caught us right in the middle of it. Then the whole five-hundred-person choir found out what happened. Her daddy flew down to talk to Dr. Brown and Brother Tom and told them they had better do something to punish me. If they didn't make me quit the ministry, he threatened to make a big scandal of it."

"So what did Dr. Brown say?"

"He told me I had to resign from the church immediately before the people found out and that I should tell you what happened at the convention, or they would call you in and tell you themselves. I couldn't bear to let you find out from them, so I decided to tell you myself."

I wanted to cry. I wanted to run. I wanted to pretend this wasn't really happening to me. But it was. And I had to face it. I didn't want it all to be true, but I knew it was.

"Dear God, help me." My silent panic-prayer went up; José drove on in silence. I sat there for a few minutes, trying to put it all together. My brain unlocked from its panic position, and I began to think.

"You just told me this because they forced you to, didn't you?" I said.

"Yes," José answered, hesitantly.

"You've been back home for over ten days, and you have never once come to me to tell me what had happened, which leads me to believe that you're only telling me because you had to."

He didn't say a word. We drove on in silence. My brain moved to its logical conclusion.

"If you only told me about this incident because you were forced to, what else is there?"

"What do you mean, what else is there?" he asked, feigning nonchalance.

"I mean, who else have you been with?"

"What do you mean, who else have I been with?"

"Exactly what I'm asking. If you only told me about the girl at the convention because you were forced into it, and if you had no intentions of letting me know about it, how many other women have there been that nobody has forced you to tell me about?"

"I don't see what that has to do with anything. Here I am, having to resign from the ministry and bring you my dirty laundry, and you're asking who else I've been with?"

"Yes, I am. I have to know. You didn't come home from the convention brokenhearted and repentant. You didn't come to me begging forgiveness. No. You were counting on me never finding out. Well, I can't live like that. I trusted you. Now I don't even know who you are."

"I don't want to hurt you any more than I have already, Helenita," he said sheepishly.

"I don't think you could. This is awful. But I must know who else you have been with."

"Don't ask me that, Princess!" he begged.

"I have to. Don't you see that I have to know the truth? I have to know who else you have been with, or I can't stay with you. I can't live with the unknown. At least, if I know the truth, I'll have a choice. If I don't, we don't have a chance."

"We have a chance. We can make it."

"Look, José," I said, unrelenting, "if you don't tell me exactly who you've been with, how can I go to church on Sunday and face the women. I'd be forever asking myself *How about this one?* and *How about that one?* I wouldn't be able to trust any woman we know. I wouldn't be able to face any woman without wondering if she was thinking what a fool I was. I can't shut myself off from other people. I have to go out there and face them. You can't do this to me. I have to know."

By this time, he had already signaled his exit off the freeway, and we were almost back at the parsonage. The town looked so dreary now. The sunny fields had lost their luster, the buildings floated by in a haze, and people without faces moved aimlessly down the streets around us. He pulled into the parsonage lawn and shut off the engine.

"Let's go inside," I said. "It's too hot out here."

We made our way through the big wooden house that seemed so empty now. Our footsteps reverberated on the wooden floors. We sat down on the plastic parsonage couch. I wouldn't let him off the hook. I was determined to know the truth.

Slowly, it came out, one sordid story after another. The large-breasted lady in the choir where we had so proudly sung *The Messiah*; members of the church; an old lady he was giving Spanish lessons to in the retirement home; a woman off the street whom he had picked up while I was out of town at a seminar; the retired lady who had donated the sofa in California.

He named about a dozen women. My mind went from one state of shock into another as I realized that even the syphilis diagnosis had been accurate. Finally, he became quiet again.

"And what about Madeleine?" I asked about my best friend, who had spent three months in the parsonage with us.

"What about her?" he asked.

"Did you have an affair with her while she was staying with us?" Scenes of Madeleine's stay flashed through my mind. Memories of that sinking feeling when I had felt something was badly wrong, but I just couldn't put my finger on it or even acknowledge my own worst fears. Memories of my suspicions and of my efforts to put them out of my mind.

"Why do you have to bring Madeleine into this?" he asked, giving me the runaround again.

"Did you have an affair with Madeleine?"

"Please don't do this to yourself, Helenita. Isn't what you've heard enough?"

"Nothing is enough until it is all out. Did you have an affair with Madeleine?"

"Don't make me say it, Helenita. Don't do this to me."

"José, I have to know. I just have to."

"Madeleine was the first. After that, it was downhill all the way."

I remembered Madeleine in a bathing suit and pictured her naked. She was so fat. Her pink flesh was flabby and puckered from cellulite. How could he have possibly preferred her over me?

Betrayed by my best friend. Betrayed by my husband. How much worse could it get?

He started to sob. I got up and walked to the kitchen. I stared out of the window for a long time. A lonely tear trickled slowly down my cheek. I felt hot, stunned, drained. The future didn't exist; today, I was suspended in a timeless void. I couldn't even imagine what I would do with this information. I had no idea.

"Would you like something to eat?" I finally asked.

"No," he said. "Just a glass of water."

I took him the glass of water and sat back down.

"How could you do this to me, José?" I cried. "I loved you! I trusted you! I gave you my life, my innocence, my virginity, my all."

There was no adequate answer. He sat defeated at the other end of the plastic couch. His head hung in shame. His face bathed with tears.

"I never meant to hurt you," he said. "Will you ever be able to forgive me?"

"I don't know. I just don't know what I'll do."

That night we lay at opposite sides of the lonely bed, no longer hugging one another's warmth as we normally did. The bridge of trust had been broken. Now I knew what he had been hiding from me for so long, and it hurt. I cried myself to sleep, wondering how this could ever be as small as a speed bump.

The next morning, I took his car and drove to work as if I were a zombie. Everything seemed gray and moving in slow motion. I was numb and couldn't feel a thing. People moved around me as if in a dream. I made my calls as if on remote. Only momentarily, in the health-food store, did reality try to creep up on me. I started to cry, but I had to hold myself together.

"God help me," my soul cried out, as if in a fog, while hour after hour dragged on.

Back at the parsonage, José refused to eat for three days. He lay in his bed crying crocodile tears of remorse and begging me not to leave him.

How could I leave him? Where would I go? What would I do? I couldn't even think that far ahead. I just had to concentrate on making it through the next five minutes without breaking down.

CHAPTER 26

Life after that was not easy. For a while, I lived as if in a dream. The denominational leaders took it for granted that I would divorce José immediately. I wasn't sure what I would do, and I was too ashamed to talk to anyone about it. Most often, I just wished desperately that he would be killed in a car wreck and I would be free of him, because I didn't have the courage to divorce him.

José quietly resigned from his job, and we moved out of the parsonage. We still had the mobile home, and I still had my job. In an effort to avoid confronting the future, I worked harder at my career than ever.

On weekends, we drove several hours over the border into Mexico to go to church. José had a close friend there, and he didn't feel comfortable going anywhere locally for fear of recognition. The congregation in Mexico met in a school classroom. It was charismatic, and often there were messages from God in tongues and interpretation. Even though no one knew about our problems, José received several interpreted messages urging him to turn to the Lord and straighten his ways. They seemed to have no impact on him at all.

"Let's leave Texas," José said finally, one day.

"Leave Texas? Why? What's the problem?" I asked, surprised.

"I don't know. I feel uncomfortable here. You never know who's talking about you. Every now and then I see people in the grocery store looking at me. I think they must know. They must be talking about me. Some of them may have seen me when I was on television. Others may have heard what happened."

His sensitivity to criticism surprised me, since only a few Saturdays earlier, while at a garage sale, he had openly bought a whole stack of pornographic magazines.

"I can't believe you did that!" I had said, hurrying in shame to get back in the car. "People around here know that you're a minister."

"So?" he had said, looking at me defiantly.

"Someone may recognize you, and what will they think, if they see you with pornographic magazines in your hand?"

"Let them think what they want! I don't care!"

But he did care, and he wanted to escape.

"We've always wanted to go to graduate school to further our studies in theology," José was saying. "This seems the perfect opportunity to get away and start over. I'll take Greek, and you'll take Hebrew. It'll be a fresh start."

We applied and were both accepted at Redeemer Seminary in Kansas. We sold the mobile home and applied for grants and loans. I told my boss that I was quitting to get my master's degree. She probably would have been very understanding, but I was too embarrassed to tell her the truth.

We used some of the proceeds from the mobile home to take a long vacation and drove as far as we could from our problems. José promised life would be different now, and we would start afresh and live happily ever after. I believed him. I knew that forgiveness was a choice, and I made that choice. I wanted our marriage to succeed. I loved him. I couldn't envision life without him, and I was prepared to start over as if nothing had ever happened.

We laughed, and talked, and kissed. He was euphoric and grateful to be forgiven; I was relieved and comforted to have him back. Having rebonded emotionally, we returned home, packed our belongings into a rental van, and moved to Kansas.

Being in graduate school was exciting. There were so many interesting classes, so many fascinating lecturers, so many stimulating discussions. The professors came from theologically varied backgrounds, and they opened up a world of freedom compared to the denominational rigidity we had experienced in our former seminary classes while pastoring.

The campus was beautiful. I would often go for long walks and revel in the beauty of the parks and buildings, dreaming about possible future ministries. Hope rose in my heart that we would be able to live out our married life as if the past were truly gone. I prayed that someday even the sordid memories would evaporate, and we would truly be able to forget. After all, others had overcome similar problems, so why couldn't we?

One day, as I was walking on one of the huge lawns of the campus, I saw a vision. I saw a sunny, green field, full of wildflowers. There was a well-defined path, big enough for two, winding its way through the flowers. It was beautiful.

"What does this mean?" I asked the Lord.

"This is your life," He replied. And it was. My life was full of promise and beauty. The future looked enticingly good. I could see myself with José walking along happily, hand in hand. Life seemed great.

Suddenly, in the distance, appeared a huge black mountain. It grew and grew and became blacker and blacker.

"What is that?" I asked, startled.

"It's a big problem," the Lord replied. I shuddered. The mountain looked foreboding. He led me closer to the mountain.

"There is a very huge problem that is coming your way."

"What is it?" I asked.

"You will know when it appears," He said.

"How can this problem be overcome?" I asked.

"Only through faith. If you and José both have faith, there is an elevator that can take you halfway up the dark mountain."

"And then what?"

"You'll see when you get there."

I hid the vision in my heart. It wasn't long before it came to pass.

Physical fitness was a required part of the school curriculum. I enjoyed swimming, and José sometimes went to the gym at night to catch up on his running. He usually left at six and was back by seven-thirty.

One evening he tarried, arriving home at almost ten o'clock. I was sitting on the sofa, studying, when he walked in the door.

"You'll never believe where I've been!" he said jubilantly, tossing his sports bag on the kitchen table.

"Oh? Where's that?" I asked, trying not to let my aggravation at his thoughtlessness show.

"I went to Sheree's house!"

"Who's Sheree?" I questioned, somewhat disturbed at this turn of events.

"Oh, she's a girl I saw at the gym. She invited me to her house, and I got to meet her mother. They want us both to come and have lunch with them on Sunday."

I was getting mixed signals. I didn't know what to make of the situation, but I put it out of my mind and decided that on Sunday, I would find out who this Sheree was, and why her mother was being so hospitable.

Sheree lived in a fine house in a beautiful suburb nearby. Her mother, a tall, elegant, blonde opened the door and introduced herself warmly.

Sheree was right behind her. She was about my height. Her hair was about my color. Her skin was fair, and her eyes were hazel. She looked young and innocent. I learned that she was studying Spanish and was eager to visit Latin America. In short, she was a younger version of me.

There were several other guests there for lunch. The conversation flowed pleasantly, and for a while, I almost thought that we were at an innocent Christian gathering.

"Why don't you gentlemen visit in the game room, while the ladies and I go to the parlor," said Sheree's mother, when the meal was over.

That sounded like a nice idea, so Sheree, her mother, a couple of other women, and I retired to an adjacent room. Sheree's mother closed the door, and we exchanged pleasantries over a cup of hot tea.

Suddenly, Sheree's mother cleared her throat, and everyone became very silent.

"I need to say something to you, Helen," said Sheree's mother, looking me straight in the eye. I felt as if a knife had gone through my heart. Subconsciously, I already knew what she was going to say. I braced myself not to fall apart. Sheree shifted awkwardly on the sofa.

"Your husband has been pursuing my daughter," she said.

She paused.

"He has been following her everywhere: to the library, the gym, and on the school grounds. He is a married man, and this simply has to stop."

I was mortified. I was embarrassed to be sitting in this genteel living room with such fine people, only to be told what a scumbag I had for a husband. I felt responsible for what he was doing and for the distress he was causing her. The pain hurt so bad. We had come to seminary to start a new life, and here I was, facing a situation I thought I would never have to face again.

"I am so concerned about the problem," Sheree's mother continued, "that if José so much as approaches my daughter again, I will report him to the dean, and he will be expelled. I am on the board of directors and know several of the professors personally. They will listen to me. I just wanted to tell you, in case you didn't know what was going on."

"I'm so sorry," I stammered. I felt like a fool for the second time.

"We know it's not your fault, dear," continued Sheree's mother, reading from my face what a painful situation I was in. "But things are getting quite out of hand, and I will not tolerate it."

"Thank you for telling me," was all I could say. "Maybe we should go home now."

My heart was heavy as we drove away silently. I told José about our conversation in the parlor. He seemed quite unconcerned.

"You know how protective mothers are, Princess!" he said. "Sheree's mother is just overreacting. Nothing is going on between us!"

We talked. He promised to give me no cause for concern. He said he had the faith to make our marriage work. That must have been what the vision meant about going halfway up the mountain in an elevator.

So I asked the Lord what to expect when we got out of the elevator. The vision opened up again, as if in a movie. This time, the scene was bleak. The mountain was in deep shadow. The climb appeared steep and almost insurmountable. There were no easy paths, no shortcuts, just strenuous climbing.

My life was such hard work now. I kept on going. I was so very, very tired. One day, I took a walk around the campus to talk to the Lord.

"I am so tired of holding on. I'm afraid I'll fall," I told Him. A picture came to mind of a sheer rock face with tall, gray pink cliffs. I looked up. The summit was so very far away. I looked down, and the fall seemed deadly.

"I'm hanging on to the rope, but I'm so afraid I'll fall," I said.

"You won't," He replied. "You'll only dangle, because the rope is anchored securely at the top."

That night, deep in his sleep, José rolled over and reached out to me.

"Sheree! Oh, Sheree! I love you, Sheree!" he mumbled, and my heart broke.

I couldn't concentrate on my studies anymore. I would burst into tears every time I went to the restroom. I couldn't stop myself from crying as I walked down the hallways. I sat in the back row in the hopes that other students would not see the tears plopping down on my notepad. I started to fear for my sanity.

José had always said that if I told a single soul about his infidelities, he would leave me, but I could hold it in no longer. I applied for counseling sessions through the seminary and was awarded two free hours a week.

Talking to Alice in the secrecy of her private office, looking into her sympathetic brown eyes, and hearing the words of torment wrench loose from my imprisoned soul, was the balm I needed to keep my sanity and continue with my studies. Week after week, I poured out my troubles, and slowly, but surely, I began to realize how emotionally bankrupt I was.

José was distant now. He was angry that I was going to counseling but not angry enough to follow through with his threat of divorce. He rarely hugged me and never showed signs of affection. He slept on the library couch during the day instead of studying, and I wondered what was wrong with him. I began to feel very lonely. His family was so far away. Mine was on the other side of the world. We were living in limbo without the comfort and support of anyone from our past.

One evening, a group of students came to our apartment for a class project. José invited them into the living room. A young man sat down beside me, and during the conversation, he patted my knee twice—pat, pat—in acknowledgement of something I had said.

As soon as the door closed behind the last visitor, José let it rip. He accused me of having an affair with Rob and being no better than he. At night, the bed seemed blacker than ever, and though I could hear his breathing, I felt more alone than I could stand.

The next morning, I dressed and walked to the library. As I passed the door to the research room, I saw Rob through the glass window. I had never noticed him before, and I was sure that his gesture the night before had been totally innocent. But at that moment, such a longing for love suddenly hit me. I was starved for affection. I wished Rob would talk to me, listen to me, love me. The longing was so deep, it burned as fire in my body, and I ran so as not to succumb.

For three days, I burned with desire. Several times I purposely passed by the little glass window and looked inside. But always I tore myself away, praying for the strength to resist.

I knew I had no business with Rob. I knew that we, indeed, had nothing in common. Yet maybe he, too, was in a position of need, and some unspoken message had passed between us.

In my memory, I heard the words of the Book of Proverbs about the ravages of adultery.

> Can a man take fire in his bosom, and his clothes not be burned? Can one go upon hot coals, and his feet not be burned? . . . But whoso committeth adultery . . . lacketh understanding: he that doeth it destroyeth his own soul. A wound and dishonour shall he get; and his reproach shall not be wiped away. (Prov. 8:27–28, 32–33 KJV)

The verses about resisting the devil were strongly in my conscience.

> . . . the devil prowls around like a roaring lion looking for someone to devour. (1 Pet. 5:8 NIV)

Resist the devil, and he will flee from you. (James 4:7 NIV)

Part of me wanted to resist; yet part of me wanted to succumb. My imagination would want to carry me into Rob's arms. My will forced me to walk away resolutely.

I had always thought of temptation as being something one could dabble with, or not, at liberty. But this was an obsession. I was being carried by a force almost too strong to resist. The devil had found the vulnerable chink in my armor and decided to launch a full-fledged attack at my moment of greatest weakness.

I knelt in my living room and cried for deliverance. I pleaded with God to release me from this emotion that was tearing my guts apart. I begged Him to stop me from making the most foolish move of my life. I knew that if I just pushed open the door to the research room, it would be over for me. There would be no resisting, and Rob would not say no.

Momentarily, I would find peace; but before long, I remembered José's aloofness, my great loneliness, and the torment returned. Alone, I fought the battle until late the third day. Realizing that I had refused to give in, the Tempter left me alone.

CHAPTER 27

In the days that followed, I pleaded with God for direction. He showed me the next scene in the vision that represented my life. I saw myself on the mountain, groping to reach the summit. I was hopeful. The climb would soon be over, and life could be beautiful again. Much to my dismay, when I saw myself reaching the top, it was bleak and windy. The skies started churning, and the clouds thickened. The wispy grass blew in the cold, harsh wind.

Valentine's Day came. José and I went to our new church for a special service. After the sermon, the pastor invited all the couples to come to the altar for a reconsecration. I could see couples ahead of us gently touching each other, holding hands, or hugging on their way to the altar. My heart leapt in hope. But when our turn came to step forward, José moved into the aisle without me. I followed and tried to take his hand. He pulled it away.

As the pastor prayed, José stood there, hard as a rock. Not a muscle flinched. I had never felt so alone and so unloved as on that Valentine's Day. When the service ended, I made my way to the altar, where I could no longer contain my sorrow. I hung over the rail, sobbing. After dismissing all the people, the pastor returned to turn out the lights and saw me there.

"Is there anything I can help you with, Helen?" He asked. I dare not speak. I couldn't tell him that I was a graduate student of theology and that my husband, a fellow student and minister, didn't love me anymore.

The pastor stayed with me a long time. He put his hand on my shoulder and prayed a soothing prayer. The longer he prayed, the louder I sobbed. I didn't think I would ever get over it. José hovered nearby to make sure I wouldn't speak out and embarrass him.

"What do I do now?" I asked the Lord, in desperation.

"This is the time when you have to fly as an eagle," He replied. "Eagles capitalize on the force of the wind to carry them to greater heights than they ever could on their own. Faith is like that. You have to spread your wings, and let the wind carry you." I didn't have much strength left, so I asked the Lord to carry me and give me the faith to fly as an eagle.

My sessions with Alice were a great help, and the environment at the seminary was so uplifting that, despite my inner heartbreak, I found much joy in attending classes and studying such interesting topics. Even in the women's preaching class, they said I was very good, and the professors all seemed pleased with my progress.

In the next scene of my vision, I saw a village in the distance. It was in a shadow and uninviting, but it was sheltered from the wind and provided refuge and rest. I looked forward to a time of rest in real life, and it soon showed up in the form of a vacation. At the Easter break, we flew back to Mexico City to be with José's family. The vacation was unremarkable, but it did provide just the rest that I needed. José's family was delighted that we were in seminary, and José, as usual, entertained them every evening with his charismatic personality.

We returned to class and started studying for the final exams. It was then that José was caught with Sheree again. I never did find out the circumstances, but Sheree heeded her mother's warnings and reported José's advances to her. She, in turn, went to the dean and requested José's removal from seminary.

I feared that the end was near, and I went to see the counseling supervisor, who interviewed us separately in a last attempt to save our marriage.

"What is your diagnosis?" I asked him in confidence.

"Your husband is a pleasure addict," he explained. "He is compulsive, just as drug and alcohol abusers. His way of asserting himself is by seducing women. It is possible that compared to you, he feels insecure in the United States and in graduate school. His way of overcoming his inadequacies is typical of Latin men. He must prove to himself that he can still conquer women. It doesn't necessarily mean that he loves them. He just wants to get them into bed to prove to himself that he is still capable."

"Can he change?" I asked, holding my breath for the most critical answer of all.

"In my professional and missionary experience, there is less than a 2-percent chance of his ever changing."

I was quiet for a long time, trying not to cry. The finality of the information was sinking in.

"What are you going to do?" the counselor asked.

"I don't know. I'm so emotionally drained; I don't have the strength to do anything."

"So what's it going to take, Helen?" he asked, waiting for my reply.

"I don't know what to do. I just don't know what to do . . ." I murmured.

"Well, if you don't know what to do at this time, I have some very practical advice for you: go back and suffer some more, until you can suffer no more!" he said.

"I can't take much more."

"Well, when you can't take any more, you'll do something to change the situation."

At about that time, I went for a routine physical at the seminary clinic. In reviewing my medical history, the Christian physician was taken aback to see that I had had syphilis.

"The Bible is very clear, Helen. Women are to be submissive to their husbands, regardless of the conditions of the marriage. Even if he gives you venereal disease over and over again, it is your Christian duty to stay with him and keep loving and forgiving him, no matter what he does. You never know when he may turn around."

Deep down I rebelled. How dare this man preach to me about what my Christian duty was! Not even God would want me to live a life of subjection to this kind of misery. Why couldn't men be held responsible for their actions, and why would Christianity condemn abused women to a living hell, and even possible death? What kind of dream world was this man living in that he would have the audacity to advise me to take such risks? No, I could not accept what the physician was saying as Christian. It just didn't ring true at all. Jesus Himself allowed for divorce in cases of infidelity. Why couldn't Christians?

I was so exhausted from trying to make the marriage work, that I wanted to know from God what the future would be like.

"What awaits me in my life with José?" I begged of the Lord.

He showed me the final scene of the vision. Beyond the restful village, I could see endless horizons of purple and blue mountains. Fold after fold, the mountains were not quite as black as the one I had just climbed, but they were dull gray and misty purple, continuing on into infinity.

To me, it just looked like more of the same. Forever.

It was time to face reality. It was time to start making some decisions about my future.

I had always been told that God has a plan for my life. I thought of that plan as a series of actions that I was to take, and if I ever missed the way, I would have missed God's best for me. After that, I would have to be content with God's second best. I believed that God had only created one man for me, and if I left him, there would be nobody else. I had not yet understood God's mercy.

In one of our classes, the professor challenged my view of God's guidance.

"If you have a child, do you expect your child to choose the career you have planned for him, marry the woman you have selected for him, live in the town you think is the best for him, and accept only the promotions that you approve?"

"No, of course not," I answered, automatically.

"Wouldn't you wish instead for your child the happiness, maturity, and freedom to make his own choices, and even change his mind if he didn't like the way things were going?"

"Of course, I would!"

"Could that not mean, then, that God's plan for us is freedom and fulfillment, and He lets us choose the details for ourselves?"

"I never thought of it that way," I said. I left the classroom deep in thought and meditated on that possibility for a long time. Maybe I shouldn't always be asking God, "What do you want me to do?" Following the professor's logic, maybe God was asking me, "What do you want to do?"

What did I want to do? It had been so long since I had considered my own wishes, that I really had no clue what I wanted to do. The very idea that I might be able to have a say in what I wanted to do about my own life was completely new. I had been an independent young woman in my single years, but somehow, I had the idea that in marriage, one renounces one's own desires in subjugation to one's husband's. I was emotionally bankrupt, and I had forgotten how to dream.

Yet Jesus did tell his disciples, "You are no longer my servants; you are my friends." (John 15:15 NIV paraphrased) Maybe it was time for me to stop thinking of myself as a powerless puppet in God's hands and at the mercy of my husband, and consider the possibility of becoming responsible for my life and for the choices that I made.

Did I really want to be married to José? Could I live with his infidelities for the rest of my life? Was he making any serious attempts to change? Was he even a participant in our marriage vows?

I saw for the first time that just as I had chosen voluntarily to be married, I could choose to end the marriage. I would not, in fact, be ending it. José already had. All I would be doing was declaring that to be a fact.

"When did it go wrong?" I asked José, in bed one night.

"When there was no blood on the wedding night," he answered.

Six-and-a-half years into our marriage, I realized that I had never had a chance. He had never believed that I was uniquely his. He had used that as his justification not to be uniquely mine. It had been over before it had ever begun, and I was only just now seeing it.

I made an appointment to see a divorce lawyer. He explained that since I was a resident of Texas, I would have to go back to Texas before I could get a divorce.

Meanwhile, the dean called me in for a private conference.

"Sheree's mother has informed us of your husband's activities, and we are going to have to expel him from the school. However, we know that you have been going to counseling and trying to make it through very difficult circumstances, so for your sake, if you will both quietly leave as soon as the exams are over, we will spare you the embarrassment of expelling José."

I thanked the dean, went home, and called Debbie, my old boss at the employment agency. I told her that we couldn't afford to stay in school any more and were thinking of moving back to Texas.

"I have a new office in San Antonio," she said right away. "I'll fly you to Texas to look at it, and maybe you'll accept the manager's position."

CHAPTER 28

I knew even as I put the phone down that I would accept Debbie's offer. I would come down to look at her office, and then I would lease an apartment in my name only. I was too ashamed to tell her that I was planning to get a divorce. José stayed at the seminary while Debbie flew me down for my interview.

San Antonio was a clean, cosmopolitan town of a million residents, with a strong Hispanic presence. Despite the bustle of city life, it managed to maintain a relaxed, southern feeling with plenty of trees and greenery. There were oak hills in the north, and lush, mesquite-covered plains in the south. Everywhere she drove, I saw pockets of new residential construction, interspersed with huge shopping malls, movie theaters, and every kind of restaurant imaginable.

When I told José that I had accepted the job in San Antonio, and that I planned to move without him, he was furious. He whined and pleaded.

"You need me to help drive the furniture truck. There's no way you can haul it and the car alone."

I wished I had the strength to protest, but I didn't; so when the semester ended, I found myself in the rental truck beside José, driving to San Antonio. My plan was to divorce him as soon as I possibly could.

We had just enough cash to put down on the apartment and the necessary utilities. We still had $1,000 in savings in an out-of-town account.

"I know what!" said José, as he was driving happily down the highway toward San Antonio. "Let's take all the money we have and go to Israel! It'll be like a second honeymoon!"

"We can't do that! I just accepted a job, and the money we have will soon be gone when we retain our apartment. How can we possibly go to Israel and spend it all? We'd have nothing left to start over when we came back! Besides, what we have won't even cover the trip to Israel!"

"See how negative you are, Helena? You just drag me down. Every time I have a great inspiration, you say no. You have no faith. If we go to Israel, when we return, God will provide!"

"We can't keep looking to your family to bail us out. They have been so good to us, but they aren't rich. God has provided for us by giving us exactly what we need until I receive my first paycheck. I hope by then, you will have a job too. We can't just throw the money away on a vacation!"

"See? You're always so negative," he said, walking off in disgust. "You keep holding me back!"

As soon as my first lunch hour came, I rushed to the nearest bank and arranged for the $1,000 to be wired to an account in my name only. At least that way, the money would be safe, and we would have something to pay our bills with. I asked the teller not to disclose the existence of the account to anyone, and she assured me that it was totally confidential.

I also rented a safety deposit box at the bank. I had several pieces of antique jewelry, some of it dating back to the 1600s, that had been handed down in my family for generations. Many of the pieces were of Czech garnet. Some were studded with diamond chips. Each of my grandmothers had delighted in giving me a piece of jewelry on my birthdays. My parents had kept the jewelry from me for years, until they realized that my marriage to José was permanent. Then they had turned it over to me. The pieces had sentimental value to me, and I didn't want anything to happen to them.

We had no trouble finding a church we liked, and we were there whenever the doors opened. One Wednesday evening, as we drove back to the apartment after the midweek prayer meeting, I realized we were out of bread.

"I'll drop you off and run down to the supermarket to buy a loaf of bread. We need it for breakfast tomorrow," I volunteered.

"All right," José said, "but hurry right back." His tone was unusually insistent.

"Well, of course; it'll only take me about twenty minutes." I had no reason to delay, but what was the rush?

By a quarter of ten, I was back. I locked the door for the night and put the bread in the refrigerator.

Suddenly, José walked right by me in his best Sunday suit, opened the front door and walked out, locking the door behind him. I rushed to the front door and stepped out onto the balcony. I caught a glimpse of him as he climbed into the car in the parking lot below and drove quickly away.

What's going on? I thought. *Where is he going? He never just walks out, especially not at bedtime! Where could he be going at this time of night without even saying a word?*

A feeling of panic swept over me. I began to sweat. My head was reeling.

No. I had to control myself. I couldn't let myself get into an emotional frenzy.

Don't jump to conclusions, I told myself. *Stay calm. There will probably be a logical explanation.* I forced myself to lie down between the sheets. *Try and sleep*, I told myself. *It's important for you to act as if nothing is wrong.*

I left the Chinese lantern on to keep me company and willed myself to sleep. From time to time, I rolled over and opened my eyes. There was nobody there beside me. The hours dragged by.

Stay calm, Helen; don't get upset. Until you know exactly where he is, there's no point getting hysterical, I told myself.

At a quarter past three, I heard a key in the door. I wondered what to do.

Keep calm. Don't say a word, I thought to myself, the tension rising in my abdomen.

I wondered what would happen next. I lay still without moving a muscle. I heard the shower come on, a long shower with lots of soap.

He has never showered that long, I thought. *Why is he soaping himself down so much?*

Finally, he lay down on the sheets.

"Hi," I said, feigning normalcy. "Where have you been?"

"Oh, to the drive-in movies," he answered, without hesitation.

"Who with?"

"I found out that you had transferred our money into an account in your name. I was mad. I wanted to get back at you. I picked up a woman at the quick-shop on the corner earlier today. I told her I would take her to the drive-in tonight. She lives close by."

The tears trickled down my cheek.

Don't say a word, I told myself. *Keep control of your emotions.*

An hour later, my body exploded from the tension, and I was doubled over the toilet, vomiting violently. José said he felt sorry for me; I looked so vulnerable. He said he was sorry.

The next morning, as I walked alone on the golf course nearby, the tears poured down my face as I reflected on the true meaning of love. A poem emerged from my broken heart:

Love is not my feelings,
Love is not my words.
Love is my commitment
Followed by my acts.
My acts must be consistent,
Or love is not at all.
Words and feelings will not prove it,
But my life will tell it all.

José knew how to fill my life with beautiful words and feelings; but just as he knew how to flatter me, he knew how to flatter other women also, and I was sick of it. Literally.

For several years, I had felt as if I was living under a curse, moving from church to church, and from disaster to disaster. Now I *knew* that I had been. José had brought upon himself the wrath of God, and I had been the recipient of that judgment by association.

Yet it had not all been bad. I had enjoyed married life—the companionship, the sharing, the teamwork, the common goals. I wanted that to continue, but it was clear that I could not have it with José anymore. Even though I loved him and was profoundly emotionally connected to him, I knew that I had to make a break and leave him.

Would it be possible to find true love and companionship ever again? Was there anyone out there with whom I could be happy? I turned to God with one last cry of my heart: "Surely, God. Surely, somewhere out there, you can find me a good ole Texas boy who can treat me like a lady!"

CHAPTER 29

Even though I had made up my mind to divorce José, I still wasn't emotionally and financially strong enough to start the legal proceedings, so the status quo continued, and José remained in my apartment.

While I worked at Debbie's office, he would sit at home, reading the classified ads in the newspaper. Every now and then, he would apply for a job. Occasionally, he even took a job; but it would only last for a couple of days, and then he'd quit. Finally, he decided to buy used clothing at garage sales to resell in Mexico City.

In the meantime, we received a call for help from Consuelo, the single mother who had been excommunicated from our church in Corpus because of her fornication. I was surprised that she turned to us. She was desperate to get away from a violent man, so we helped her move to San Antonio. We found her an apartment at the other end of our complex, and she went to work sewing at a blue jean factory on the other side of town.

José was planning his first trip to Mexico City when I stubbed my toe and couldn't walk. He insisted on leaving anyway. He took what cash we had, and I had to ask Consuelo to come over and pawn our television to buy me some food. Fortunately, I didn't have to touch my heirloom jewelry.

When José returned from Mexico, the oil and gas crisis was at its worst, and the employment business crashed as a result. I left Debbie's employment and became a traveling sales representative for a large photographic company. José was thrilled that I had flexible hours, because he planned for us to return to Mexico City for Christmas.

"How can we afford to keep going all the way to Mexico City," I asked, "when I'm just starting a new job?"

"Oh, have faith, Helenita! We can sell some more clothes. Anyway, I have to be with my family at Christmastime, and I want to buy them some Christmas presents. I want to go to your safety deposit box and pull out your jewelry, so we can pawn it over Christmas," he said enthusiastically. "My mother really needs a new steam iron, and I want to bring everyone a nice gift, so they can see how well we are doing in the United States."

I protested, but he insisted. So I sat in the car, watching him run in and out of the pawn shops, negotiating for good deals on my family jewelry. Finally, he returned in triumph with enough money for gas and gifts. We drove to Mexico City for the holidays, and he proudly presented his mother with a steam iron from K-Mart.

When it was time to return, José had yet another great idea.

"Paco has invited me to preach at our old church in San Martín for the next two Sundays. I'll help you drive up to the border so you can go back to work, and I'll take the train back down here."

The drive to the border was long and arduous. Just before entering the United States, I dropped him off at the railway station. He was wearing the same blue suit he wore when I first met him and his large, straw cowboy hat. He kissed me goodbye and stood smiling and waving happily as I drove away.

It was eight o'clock in the evening when I crossed over the bridge into Texas. I had already been driving for two days straight, and several hours driving along a lonely highway lay before me. It was January and bitterly cold. If I turned on the heat to stay warm, I couldn't keep my eyes open, but when I turned the engine off and curled up to go to sleep, it soon became too cold, and I woke up shivering. In fits and starts, I finally made it home in the wee hours of the morning.

Heavy boxes of photographic equipment began to arrive from my new employer. We lived on the second floor, so I had to haul them all up the stairs by myself. One day Arthur, a friend of ours, stopped by. We were new in town, so we didn't know anyone very well, but Arthur had come by the apartment a couple of times to visit with us. He seemed like a very sweet person, always eager to help his fellow man.

"Let me give you a hand in getting those upstairs," he said automatically, when he saw me struggling with the boxes. When he finished, I crossed the street to his car. He took my elbow like a gentleman to protect me from the traffic. Something inside me snapped.

Where was José when I needed him? He wasn't there to help me with the heavy boxes. He wasn't there to make a living and help me with the bills. He wasn't there to laugh or keep me company. He wasn't even there to hold me when I cried. What on earth was he good for anyway?

I went inside and called the seminary to talk to my counselor, Alice.

"What's going on?" she asked. I gave her a brief synopsis of the last seven months.

"It sounds like just more of the same, Helen," she said.

I hung up the phone, her words reverberating in my ears. She was right. Nothing had changed. I had been deceiving myself because I had been too drained to end the marriage. Why had I not been able to see it before?

Even though it was Saturday morning, I opened the telephone directory, called a lawyer, and insisted on an immediate appointment to initiate divorce proceedings that very day. Two hours later, I was in the lawyer's office. He told me that he would file the papers first thing Monday morning, and sixty days later, I would be free. José would have no recourse whatsoever.

On Tuesday evening, José was scheduled to call at six o'clock to let me know whether he was ready to come home. The phone rang precisely on the hour. I was waiting. José greeted me triumphantly.

"I borrowed fifty-thousand pesos from Paco and bought a Volkswagen bug! It's yellow, and it runs great. I've finished preaching here, and I'm ready to come home!"

"Well, don't bother," I answered, wondering what possessed him to buy a used car in Mexico when we lived and worked in the United States. "I've filed for divorce," I continued. "This is the State of Texas, so it'll be final in sixty days, and there's absolutely nothing you can do about it."

It felt good to have made the decision. It felt good to know that, for once, he was powerless against me.

José began to cry, stunned by my news.

"Don't leave me, Helenita, please. I'll do anything."

"It's done," I said, "and I'm not changing my mind."

"But I love you, Little Princess," he sobbed. "We are so good together. I promise I'll never hurt you again."

"It's too late, José. I've made up my mind."

"I never thought it would come to this. Won't you please reconsider. I'll do anything, anything to get you back!"

"No. It's done, and I will not reconsider. The divorce has been filed, and it will be final in sixty days."

With that, I hung up the phone and contemplated my situation. From the tone of his voice, I was sure that José would jump in the Volkswagen bug and start driving for the border. With his brother Gilberto's help at the wheel, they could drive through the night and be in San Antonio within twenty-four hours. That would be six o'clock, or so, the following evening.

I was scared. I didn't want to be caught in my apartment when he arrived. I wasn't sure what he would do. I was afraid he might be violent and beat me up. I was afraid I might lose heart and let him talk me out of the divorce. I couldn't risk seeing him again, because I was too weak to fight.

Immediately, I started packing. I called Arthur and told him what was going on. He ran to the grocery store for boxes and came right over to help. We packed all night until both our cars were crammed full.

"Try and get some sleep OK, Helen," Arthur said. "I have to go to work at eight, but if you find an apartment somewhere across town, I'll bring you what I have in my car tomorrow night."

I set the alarm for seven. By eight-fifteen, I had arranged for a mover to pick up the sofa bed, chairs and table, and the remainder of my boxes. By ten, I had found a new apartment. At noon, the movers arrived and carried everything away.

The only things left in the apartment were José's seminary books, his suits and shirts hanging neatly in the closet, and his shoes lined up in a row on the floor. I had no family this side of the Atlantic, whereas he did. After everything I had put up with, and all the money I had earned while he sat on the sofa, I decided that our meager household goods deserved to remain with me.

To be safe, I knew I had to disappear completely. I would not return to our church or speak to any of our mutual friends, because I didn't want anyone to lie about my whereabouts. I closed our bank account, canceled our lease, our phone, and our utilities. I asked my employer not to disclose my whereabouts to anyone. Since I was a traveling salesperson and worked out of my home, José wouldn't he able to look for me at work. I would be completely untraceable!

But then I remembered Consuelo. I was her only friend, and I didn't want her to go through another rejection. Somehow, I had to warn her. She wasn't allowed to receive phone calls at work, and she didn't have a phone at home. I was afraid to leave a note in case José found it. My only option was to drive to her end of the apartment complex and wait for her to drive home from work. She was due to get home at five thirty, which would give me time to warn her and get away before José arrived.

I backed my car into a secluded parking spot in a dead end between two trees at the entrance closest to her apartment. I had one hand on the horn, another on the light switch. Consuelo would be turning in from the main street and driving right past me. As soon as she appeared, I planned to honk my horn and flash my lights to catch her attention.

Then I would jump out and tell her to meet me at the Pizza Hut immediately.

Five-thirty came and went, but there was no sign of Consuelo. I began to get nervous. What could be taking her so long? What if she stopped at the store to pick up dinner? What if they let her out late? I had butterflies in my stomach. I was getting very nervous. I kept looking at my watch, because I could not take a risk. If Consuelo wasn't there by six o'clock, I'd just have to leave. It was 5:55, and there was still no sign of her.

Just then, my heart nearly stopped beating, and the hair on the back of my neck stood to attention. A yellow Volkswagen bug turned in from the main street. Immediately, I recognized José's brother, Gilberto, at the wheel, and sure enough, José was sitting right beside him.

I punched the automatic door lock and tried to slide unobtrusively down in my seat, but it was too late! José had spotted my car, and Gilberto brought the Volkswagen to an abrupt halt right in front of me, blocking my exit completely.

I froze in terror.

José opened his car door and walked toward me. He looked furious.

"We went up to the apartment, and it was locked. Let us in!" he yelled at me through my closed window.

I waved my hand to say no.

Miraculously, Gilberto thought I was waving to him to get out of the way, so I could lead them back. He inched his car forward, thus opening my way of escape!

Instantly, I turned the key in the ignition and floored the accelerator. My car jerked out of its hiding place, and I sped toward the street. José climbed back into the Volkswagen, but they were facing the wrong direction, and it would take them a while to get turned around and into the street.

Within seconds, I was in the road. I didn't even check for oncoming traffic. I just sped out of the complex and turned right onto the main street, instead of left toward our apartment. It was almost dark, and I didn't have my lights on. If only I could get to the next corner and turn down some side street again before José and Gilberto could react, I might be able to get away.

I sped down an unknown road. As soon as I could, I turned down another street, and then another. I was in such a panic that I didn't even look to see who was in the way. I kept checking my rearview mirror, but thankfully, the yellow bug was nowhere to be seen.

I reached the freeway and drove a couple of exits. Then I sped onto another freeway, weaving in and out of the traffic to thwart any chase. My heart was pounding, and I was running on pure adrenaline. I exited the freeway abruptly and rushed through a residential neighborhood, jumping curbs and turning left and right to lose my pursuers.

Finally, about eight miles from my apartment, I pulled the car to a halt on a quiet side street. My heart was pounding, my hands were shaking, but I was free!

CHAPTER 30

The next six months were the hardest of my life. I was single. I was in hiding. I had just started a new job, and I was alone. The future I had conceived in my imagination had José in every scene. With him gone, the whole picture had to be erased, and I didn't have another to take its place. My dreams were dead. All I saw was one big, empty blank.

I couldn't even contact his family, and I missed them terribly. They had been our emotional support for almost seven years. The implications of never being able to see them all again were awesome. They were probably in shock over my unexpected disappearance. I couldn't just call them up and explain my side of the story. After all, he was their son.

I made enough money to pay for my apartment and my car, but I had to go to the bank and get a loan to retrieve my jewelry that was scattered in pawn shops all over the city. I also discovered that José had defaulted in paying for the land which we had secured with my inheritance, and I had to beg and plead with the owner not to take it away from me. Mercifully, he agreed.

Thankfully, my job kept me going. Every morning, I had to get up. I had to get dressed. I had to drive to a day-care center and photograph the children. I learned to swivel around on my heels, wipe the tears from my eyes, and come back with a smile. After all, my job was to make the children laugh.

Sometimes, as I was driving down a city street, a song would play on the radio, reminding me of José, our lost love, our deleted future, the death of our dreams and our youth. I would start to cry. Sometimes, as I was crying, I couldn't remember where I was, or where I was going.

Arthur told me to keep a supply of quarters handy and call him at work when that happened. Patiently, he would ask me to look for a street sign or landmark, so he could figure out where I was. He told me to keep my day planner on the front seat, so I could see where I was supposed to be.

Sometimes I didn't even know what day it was, so my calendar was of no use; but I always remembered Arthur's phone number. Many a time, he pulled me out of my panic and depression and assured me that this, too, would pass.

Sometimes I would drive to his house and sit in my car, waiting for him to come home.

"You can't become dependent on me, Helen," he told me over and over. "You're on the rebound, and you can't afford to get involved with anyone just yet. I know you're hurt, and you're lonely, but first, you have to get well."

We had taken a course on grief in seminary, so I knew that my only hope was to go through it. I knew that if I didn't face it head on, I would be an emotional cripple for the rest of my life.

So I got angry. Angry with God.

Why had He let this happen to me when I had totally committed my life to Him? I had given up everything to go live in Mexico. Why had He allowed my husband to betray me with my best friend, whom I had led to Christ? How would I ever finish seminary? What about my calling? What about my ministry? What about my future? Just as if in a fire, everything had disappeared. All I had left were the ashes, and I sat in them, stunned, and grieving.

I found that I cried in fits and starts. Sometimes there were a few quiet tears; sometimes long, agonizing wails.

Alone in my apartment, I set up a funeral pyre. I pulled out all my photographs of José, and I yelled at him.

"How could you do this to me?" I screamed. "Can't you see what this has done to us? To me? To you? To your family? To our friends? To the church? Why, oh, why?"

I tried to punch a pillow, pretending it was José, but all I could do was break down and cry. He was gone. It was over. The wound of betrayal cut through my heart. How would I ever recover?

CHAPTER 31

Sometimes I cried a little, and sometimes I cried a lot. Sometimes I was afraid that I would cry too much and explode. Whenever I found a listening ear, I would tell my story. I told it over and over again, and each time I told it, I cried a little less.

Day after day, I struggled on. Slowly, but surely, the grief began to ebb, and every once in a while, a ray of hope shone into my aching heart. I ate sparingly, spent a lot of time alone, and cried whenever I needed to.

After several months of grieving, the day came when I had cried enough. There wasn't a tear left in me to shed. I had told my story so many times that I was getting bored with it myself. I had grieved until there was no more grief. I was finally ready to move on with my life.

I marked the occasion by going to visit an old friend who lived back in Corpus, just a few hours drive away. Judy was a fun-lover, and I liked to talk to her about new and creative things.

"I can't believe you stayed with him so long," she said when I told her what had happened. "Why do you think you married him in the first place?"

"I really think he did a sales job on me. He kept working on me and persuading me that he was the one until I succumbed. I was in a different culture and out of my comfort zone. I didn't have the courage to discuss my decision with friends, and of course, I felt tremendous loneliness since my parents had cut me out of their lives. He was charming and spontaneous and a lot of fun to be with most of the time. I did enjoy life with him, and his family was warm and accepting of me when I was emotionally orphaned."

"So he met a lot of your needs in the beginning?"

"Definitely. He taught me how to have fun in life and not be so serious. He was always telling me to leave the dishes in the sink and accompany him to a movie or for a ride to the beach. It was fun to be with him. He was a very affectionate and entertaining person to be around."

"Do you think you fulfilled his needs at the time too?"

"Oh, absolutely. He was very ambitious, and I was a great catch for him. I added status to his public life. But what really brought us together was our genuine desire to be missionaries to the Indians. That was a worthy goal, and had we remained in Mexico, we might still be married."

"So you think the move to the States hurt your relationship?"

"Not the move itself, Judy, but all the stresses that went with it: our health problems, the lack of stable finances, and above all, our forced separation from his family. I think that as his emotional support system fell away, he realized he was alone. Unaccustomed as he was to foreign travel, he fell apart. The only way he knew how to assert himself and build up his self-esteem was to seduce women. He said he didn't even love them; it was just something he did to bolster his ego."

"Well, you should have left him as soon as you found out about the affairs," said Judy.

"You're probably right, but I loved him, and at least I know I went the second mile."

"You certainly did that! I wouldn't have put up with the stunts he pulled on you. I would have been out of there in a heartbeat! In a way, you betrayed yourself by staying."

"I know. Looking back, I should have ended it sooner, but at the time, I just didn't feel I had a choice. Remember, I did not grow up in the United States where women have self-evident rights. I grew up in Europe where divorce was almost unheard of and then moved to Mexico. There, all the preachers preached submission, and women didn't have any rights. It was only when I went to counseling and began to look at how my own emotional needs weren't being met at all that I even started to consider divorce. Where I grew up, divorce was not an option, so I never even considered it. Now I'm learning that I can be a Christian and have a life that I choose and cherish, too. I don't have to kiss my own life goodbye when I say 'I do.'"

"So, what's next?"

"I want to take responsibility for my life instead of leaving it all up to God. I want to get married again, but I don't want to be looking forever! I'm not that picky. I just want to find someone decent to be happy with."

"That's fine, Helen, but if you are serious about getting married, you need to define what you are looking for."

"What do you mean?"

"Let's get a piece of paper and make a list of require-ments in a husband. After all, you want to eliminate all unacceptable traits and decide what is important to you."

"I know what's important to me, Judy. It's all I've had circling in my brain lately . . ."

"All the more reason to write it down."

Judy made it sound like fun, so we spent a delightful evening discussing the profile of the person I would be look-ing for. By the end of the evening, the list was complete.

I wanted someone with at least a doctorate, so I would feel comfortable continuing my education as the years went by. I wanted someone who made more money than I, so he wouldn't be threatened by my earnings. I wanted someone who had his own business, so my life wouldn't be controlled by the military or the government. I wanted someone who was kind and decent but not a ladies' man. I wanted some-one who was spiritual but who didn't just talk the talk. I wanted someone whose family was far away, so we could make a life of our own.

I wrote it all down on a piece of paper.

"I don't want to be looking for this man forever," I told God, as I drove away from Judy's house. "So I'm going to go out with the first twelve men that invite me out. After all, there are twelve tribes of Israel, and twelve apostles, so why not twelve new men? I don't care who they are, or what they are. I don't care how long the process takes, either. But after I have met the twelfth one, I'm going to stop and pick one. Please put them on my path and guide me as I choose!"

I felt pretty good about my decision. It had been a while since my divorce, and I was ready to look for love. I popped one of my favorite cassettes into the tape player and sang along all the way home. Sure enough, as soon as I returned to San Antonio, offers of dates started to materialize. I accepted each one graciously and without condition. I asked no questions. I made no excuses. I just went. I trusted that somewhere among the twelve, there would be a winner for me.

The new church I attended met once a month at the Majestic Theater for a special service. When that particular Sunday arrived, I put on my new salmon pink skirt and blouse and took off in good time to find a parking spot. I left the car in a safe place and started to walk toward the theater.

It was a lovely June day, with clear blue skies and a gentle breeze. I was in a good mood, eager to make new friends. I passed a church, and a couple of ushers stepped toward me and handed me a bulletin.

"You *are* coming to visit us, aren't you?" they said.

"No, actually, I'm going to the theater!" I answered cheerfully, thinking how pagan that sounded on a Sunday morning.

I turned the corner and continued walking toward the theater. Strange. There were no people outside, and when I reached the door, it was locked with no note of explanation. It was too late to look for them, so I decided to return to the church I had just passed. The ushers were still there, and they pointed me in the direction of the singles' Bible class.

The lesson had already begun, and I slipped unobtrusively into the only seat left in the circle. A fair man of slight build, in old-fashioned, Buddy Holly-type glasses, offered me orange juice and doughnuts. I was impressed by his attentiveness. When the lesson ended, and I made my way down the hall, he ran after me and handed me a torn piece of grocery bag paper with a telephone number scrawled on it in pencil.

"Here's my number," he said. "I'd like to take you to lunch sometime."

"Aren't you going to the service?" I asked.

"No, I want to go home and work in the yard."

How unspiritual, I thought. But I had agreed to make no judgments and accept all invitations, so I thanked him and handed him one of my crisp business cards in return. I noticed his eyes behind the Buddy Holly-type glasses were soft and blue.

"I'll call you!" he said, and took off down the hall. He was wearing brown polyester pants, a many-times washed beige shirt, a chartreuse tie, and dusty brown sharkskin shoes. I thought he was probably a government worker, conservative and unimaginative. But he was a man, and he wanted to take me to lunch!

As soon as I got home, there was a message on my answering machine already.

"Hi, Helen. This is Paul. We met at church this morning. I'd like to take you to lunch tomorrow. Please call me."

I picked up the phone and called right away. He gave me the name of a little restaurant around the corner from his office, and I agreed to meet him there at noon.

The next day was one of glorious, blinding sunshine. As soon as I stepped into the restaurant, I could see Paul standing on tiptoes, waving at me. I made my way to his table, and he eagerly pulled my chair back for me to sit down.

"Well, tell me about yourself," he said.

So I did.

Each time I came to a stopping point, he would ask me another leading question, and I ended up talking for most of the lunch hour. By the time the waitress came with the bill, I was convinced that Paul was the most brilliant conversationalist I had ever met!

"So how about you?" I asked, as the waitress took off with his charge card. "Are you a member of the downtown church?"

"No, actually I belong elsewhere. My teenage son, who lives with me, is out on choir tour for a few days, so I'm free! How about having dinner with me tonight?"

"Tonight?" I asked, a little surprised. "I guess that would be fine." We walked out into the hot sun, and I watched him get into an old, yellow Chrysler station wagon. He had told me he was a dentist, and his conversation revealed an alert mind, but his appearance belied his profession.

I decided to do a little detective work. I drove up and down the street looking for his office, but I couldn't find it anywhere.

"It's right behind the vet's office!" he explained that evening, amused by my obvious suspicion. "By the way, would you drop me off at my house after dinner? I just live up the street, and I walked."

I decided to take him and see where he lived. We drove up a wooded hill to a lovely residential area. We stopped in front of a nice French-style house with a large green lawn. He thanked me and got out of the car.

I didn't believe he really lived there.

"Lunch tomorrow?" he asked.

"Sure."

"OK. I'll call you."

I waited to see what he would do. He walked straight up to the front door. I watched to see if he had a key. He reached into his pocket and opened the door.

He was probably house-sitting for a friend.

The next morning I did find his dental office, but I was still very cautious. After my experience with José, I could not afford to overlook my initial gut feelings. If anything questionable were to happen, I was ready to back out at once. On the third evening, while eating at the cafeteria again, Paul looked at me with an amused expression on his face.

"Now that you've told me about all your virtues, tell me if you have any vices," he said.

I stared at him, speechless. If he meant what I thought he meant, I didn't want to have anything to do with him!

I went home and got on my knees, begging God not to let me make a horrible mistake. Having just gone through a divorce, I didn't know if I could be trusted to make the right choice. I resolved not to see him again.

About a month went by, but I couldn't forget Paul. Other men seemed so boring by comparison, so I eventually picked up the phone and called him. He invited me to a talk about the Shroud of Turin at his church the following Sunday afternoon. Afterward, he took me to his house.

As we stepped inside, I was drawn immediately to the golden glow of the kitchen lamp. There at the table was a fourteen-year-old boy industriously doing his homework.

"This is my son, Jim," Paul said, introducing me to a blond boy of slight build and hazel eyes. Jim smiled and got up to shake my hand. He was alert and well-spoken, just like his father. All of a sudden, everything looked normal. Everything felt right, and all my suspicions disappeared. I accepted Paul's invitations because I enjoyed the family atmosphere, and I thought Jim was cute. Slowly, but surely, my fear of Paul dissipated, and we were able to spend time alone without Jim.

We were in the park on a hot, sunny afternoon when he first took my hand. I had thought that love only strikes in one's youth and that any romance after the age of twenty-five must be insipid. To my surprise, the passions that stirred within me at the touch of his warm hand were more powerful than anything I had experienced in my youth. When we came into my apartment, he kissed me. I collapsed on the sofa and lay there, unable to move, until long after he had gone.

The next time he came to pick me up, I peeped through my curtains to watch him pull up. When his car turned the corner into my parking lot, and I saw him climb out and make his way toward my door, the Lord startled me as He whispered in my ear.

"Treat this man with great respect. He may one day be your husband." I was taken aback and went to the door in a pensive mood.

The following weekend, Jim and I decided it was time for Paul to get a new wardrobe. We sat him down and pulled all his clothes out of his closet. One by one, we showed him each item and got his permission to give them all to charity. Then we took him to the mall for new clothes and to the optician to get a modern pair of gold-rimmed glasses.

Paul's hygienist was furious when she saw him come to work with stylish new glasses, navy pants, and new shirt and tie.

"I've been trying for ten years to get him to change his appearance, and here you've turned him around in just a matter of weeks! He must really have a crush on you!"

CHAPTER 32

As Paul and I got closer and closer, he started to panic. "He's like a walking nerve ending," said Dave, a mutual friend of ours, when I asked him what to do next.

"Just take it slowly, Helen. Paul has been burned before, and he's terrified of getting married again."

"Why don't you join the Professional Singles Club and meet more people?" Paul urged.

I didn't want to join the Professional Singles Club and meet anybody. I hated going to cocktail parties, engaging in small talk, and I liked being with Paul. However, I had to admit that I hadn't yet gone out with twelve men, so grudgingly, I acquiesced and joined the club.

It was at one of their cocktails parties that I met Brian. Brian was standing at the vegetable table as I made my way back for a refill. As my eye caught his, something inexplicable happened between us, and all of a sudden, I believed in love at first sight. Brian was fun, and he teased me. I teased him back. He asked me to dinner, and I went several times. The chemistry was great.

Then Paul called again, and I was caught in the horribly uncomfortable predicament of going out with both of them at the same time. Fortunately, there were two staircases leading up to my apartment. Paul picked me up by the front stairs, and Brian by the back. I had to juggle my calendar carefully to make sure they never met in the middle!

I hated every minute of this two-timing. In his fear, Paul kept insisting that I learn about the American way of dating several people at once, but all it did was make me more and more upset.

At the next singles' cocktail party, I was talking to Brian when I saw Paul out of the corner of my eye. I had promised to go out with Brian afterward. Paul came up to me discreetly and lowered his voice.

"Party's incredibly boring. Want to go down to the Riverwalk and take night photos?"

That sounded like such a relief.

"Meet you outside in thirty minutes?" he asked.

I went with Brian to his store, because he had to close up for the evening. I was torn. Two men had invitations for me on the same night. I couldn't continue this torment. I had to make a choice.

On the one hand, Brian had sex appeal. On the other hand, I had little in common with him, and I just didn't feel the tenderness that I did for Paul.

"I'm sorry, Brian. I can't come by after all," I said.

"You're going with the other guy, aren't you?"

"Yes, I am, but thanks for everything."

Paul stopped insisting that I see other people, and I was glad that my mission to meet twelve men was over. I had no doubts as to whom my choice was. Yet every weekend, whenever the subject of marriage came up, Paul had a new excuse.

"You're too affectionate!" he said, one Sunday. "You can't cook!" he said, on another Sunday. "You like to go out more than I do!" was the next excuse. Every week there was a new one. Last week's shortcoming was irrelevant because each Sunday he popped up with a brand new one. I just couldn't keep up with them. It became apparent that as long as he was afraid of making a commitment, I would never be good enough.

"I'm tired of hearing about my imperfections," I told him after about the tenth excuse. "Let's just drop the subject until the first of the year, and then we can decide." So we did.

I was excited when January 1 rolled around.

"Guess what today is?" I asked Paul, with great expectation.

"Tuesday. Why?" he answered.

"It's January 1. Remember?"

"Remember what?" he asked.

"Today's the day that we were going to discuss whether we would get married!"

We were standing in the cafeteria line, and he came up with yet another new excuse.

"If you don't want to get married," I said resolutely, "I'm going to find somebody else. I love you, and I want to be with you, but if you can't decide, I'm going to move on with my life, starting tomorrow."

That wasn't what he wanted to hear, so by the time we left the cafeteria that Tuesday evening, we were engaged. We planned to pick up our marriage license on Wednesday and get married on Saturday. I booked two tickets on a Caribbean cruise departing Sunday.

San Antonio is a city with mild winters, but on that January night in 1985, so much snow fell that on Wednesday, the city was completely paralyzed. The freeways and schools were closed, and it was impossible to get to the courthouse downtown for the license. Thursday was no better. We watched television reports of city trucks sprinkling sand and salt on the roads.

Finally on Friday, we were able to drive down back roads and get our marriage license, and late that evening, the minister, who had been stranded in Kentucky, managed to fly back into town just in time to perform our wedding.

"Guess what?" I said to our friends, as I called them one by one on Saturday morning.

"What?"

"Paul and I are going to get married!"

"Congratulations! That's wonderful! Have you set a date yet?"

"Yes, tonight at 7:30. Can you come? And bring a covered dish?"

Our friends were delighted. Even my parents, who had been relieved to hear of my divorce, seemed pleased when I called them with the news. The fact that Paul was a Caucasian and a dentist seemed to satisfy them.

Paul and I spent the morning cleaning the house, and after lunch we ran out to buy a wedding band for me. Then I took off to the mall to look for a dress. By half past five, I had selected two favorites, but I couldn't make up my mind.

"Put them both on the charge card and hurry back!" said Paul, when I called him from Foley's department store. "And don't forget to buy the parts for the broken toilet!"

I picked up the dresses and drove quickly to the plumber's shop, which closed at six. I got there at five minutes till six.

"Excuse me, please," I interrupted one of the salesmen, holding out my palm with the broken pieces in it. "I'm getting married at 7:30, and our toilet is broken!" The salesman ran to help me. I arrived at the house, parts in hand, to find Paul and his best man on their knees, pinning the new curtains.

The evening was a terrific success. I was still in the bathroom getting dressed when the first guests began to arrive. I could hear the laughter and the joking as they walked in. It was so much fun.

The minister held a short ceremony on the back porch, and then we laughed and ate and took pictures. We fell into bed for a short night's sleep and flew off the next morning to our Caribbean cruise!

EPILOGUE

My marriage to Paul started me on a long road of growth and recovery. I have been learning that saying "yes" to God, and "I do" to a spouse does not mean saying goodbye to myself.

Instead of buying a new house, Paul and I agreed to invest in counseling and make it a priority to get to know one another and resolve issues from our past. It has been the best money we ever spent.

Instead of keeping secrets within the family, Paul has encouraged me to make friends and seek help outside the marriage. I have been learning to build a support structure of wonderful friends of my own, besides the ones we have in common.

Instead of suffering in silence when new problems arise, I have been learning to reach out and ask others for help.

Instead of remaining mute about the pain and embarrassment of my past, I have written this book.

Instead of withdrawing from my family of origin, I have gone back to England and shared the truth about my life with José.

Instead of continuing to feel that I am the only woman in the world to experience these problems, I have run across countless others whom I have been able to encourage in their loneliness and despair.

Instead of honoring the age-old taboo about mentioning adultery, I have begun speaking about it publicly.

Instead of trying to cope with the future alone, I have been bouncing ideas around with my friends and getting wise counsel to help me along life's way.

José left town and never came back. I have spoken to him over the phone at his mother's house and have told him that I forgive him for everything.

I've searched high and low for Madeleine to tell her I forgive her, too, but she has never been seen nor heard from since.

Dear friend,

People tell me they experience all kinds of emotions reading "Betrayal in the Parsonage." I would love to receive *your* feedback.

Also, if you send me your address, I can let you know if I'm ever to be in your part of the world. My address is:

> **Helen Hunter**
> **9859 I–10 W, Box 488**
> **San Antonio, TX 78230**
>
> **e-mail: tmc96@juno.com**

PS. If you would like to know God personally, find a quiet place and ask Him to become real to you. He hears even your silent desires. Just talk to Him. He understands you. Welcome His gift of peace and forgiveness, and invite Him to guide your life from this moment on.

Let me know *what* you decided

Helen

BETRAYAL IN
THE PARSONAGE

For your personally autographed copy send:
$12.92 (includes sales tax)
plus $4.95 shipping and handling each

34 page Discussion/Study Guide
$6.38 (includes sales tax)
plus $3.50 shipping and handling each

These prices are valid for destinations worldwide
via surface mail (5–14 day shipping time)

Please send checks or money orders in US currency to:

Light Enterprises
9859 I–10 West, Box 488
San Antonio, TX 78230, USA

or have your credit card ready and call toll free:

1-800-484-9321 code 1429
or 210-696-4495
e-mail: tmc96@juno.com

Call for quantity discounts, express shipping quotes,
and other books by Helen Hunter.